January 1991.

DESIGNING & MAKING

Malcolm Cadman and Alan Ratcliffe

Hodder & Stoughton
LONDON SYDNEY AUCKLAND TORONTO

Acknowledgements

Malcolm Cadman (BA Hons, ATC) and Alan Ratcliffe (BEd) have been teaching together at Crown Woods School, Eltham since 1982 and this book was developed from their teaching practices, principally in the ILEA schools of St Thomas Apostle RC Boys School, Peckham and Crown Woods School.

The authors would like to thank the following:
David Kellock for his original guidance; the editorial assistance of Caroline Evans and Lisa Miles; Rick Dickinson, industrial designer of Dickinson Associates, for allowing use of his detailed examples of the Sinclair pocket TV and the Cambridge Instruments portable microscope (featured in the BBC Design Awards 1990); David Doyle, former Deputy Director of ILEA Design and Technology Teachers Centre, for his ready assistance; Dwight Leatham, graphic designer, for helping with the demands of layout and typography and for use of a photocopier out of hours; the pupils of Crown Woods for their design sheets and posters; Malcolm McKenzie for his pneumatic robot.

The authors and Publishers would like to thank the following for permission to reproduce material in this volume:
HMSO/Department of Education and Science for the extract from a speech made by Sir Keith Joseph (Secretary of State for Education and Science), 1985; McIntosh and Otis Inc for the quote by Norman Bel Geddes from *Product Design As Approached* by John Lane (1934); Science of Cambridge Ltd for the extracts from the Lensman leaflet.

The authors and Publishers would like to thank the following for permission to reproduce photographs in this volume:
Action Plus (86); Allsport (54 top right, bottom left); Barnaby's Picture Library (83; 91); Bosch (107, top); Braun Electric UK Ltd (59, top); County Visuals, Kent County Council (20, bottom right; 54, top left, bottom middle and right); Rick Dickinson (9); Eastbourne Tourism and Leisure (20, top right); Electrolux (59, bottom); Finemore and Field Ltd (37); Ford Motor Company Ltd (80, bottom); Glandford Borough Council (48, bottom left); Hampton Court Palace (48, top left); Hitachi (68; 74; 80, middle); ICI Acrylics (111); London Underground (48, right); Bert Mendes (4; 18; 20, bottom left, middle; 107, bottom; 118, top, middle and bottom right; 126); Pentax UK Ltd (80, top); Sevenoaks District Council (20, top left); Yachting Monthly (57).

Every effort has been made to trace and acknowledge ownership of copyright. The Publishers will be glad to make suitable arrangements with any copyright holders whom it has not been possible to contact.

British Library Cataloguing in Publication Data
Cadman, Malcolm
  Designing and making.
  1. Design & technology
  I. Title II. Ratcliffe, Alan
  600

ISBN 0 340 50400 5

First published 1990

© 1990 Malcolm Cadman and Alan Ratcliffe

All rights reserved. No part of this publication may be reproduced or transmitted in any form or by any means, electronic or mechanical, including photocopy, recording, or any information storage and retrieval system, without permission in writing from the publisher or under licence from the Copyright Licensing Agency Limited. Further details of such licences (for reprographic reproduction) may be obtained from the Copyright Licensing Agency Limited, of 33–34 Alfred Place, London WC1E 7DP.

Typeset in Palatino by Gecko Ltd, Bicester.
Printed in Hong Kong for the educational publishing division of Hodder and Stoughton Ltd, Mill Road, Dunton Green, Sevenoaks, Kent by Colorcraft Ltd, Hong Kong.

Contents

(DT) Design and Technology

'Design is not primarily a matter of drawing but a matter of thinking. . . There is an old saying that when a thing is designed right, it looks right.'
Norman Bel Geddes, 1934. 'CDT matters because it is about designing and making, and above all about learning through doing.'
Sir Keith Joseph (Secretary of State for Education and Science), 1985.

Technology and you

When you study technology, a very important part of your study will be to design and make things. Working through Design and Technology your experience will be about solving design problems. This will help you understand more about the things that you use everyday, and also about more unusual things.

The things that you find easy and pleasant to use will probably have been well designed. You may dislike some other things, or feel uncomfortable using them. These may have been poorly designed. They may even break easily or last only for a short time.

You will find that this approach has links with other areas concerned with design and the way we manage our lives, for example, using computers and electronic information, making decisions about things we use in the home and the clothes we wear, and how items are produced, sold and bought. All these areas are relevant to designing and making.

In Design and Technology, you will be expected to think before you do. This means looking carefully at the problems you have to solve. Then, when you make your design, you will be able to choose the most suitable materials and use the correct processes to get good results.

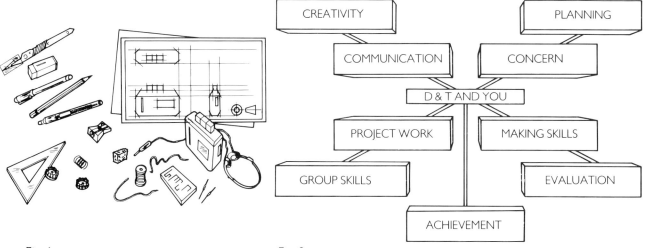

Fig. 1   Fig. 2

Designing and Making for the National Curriculum

In your school you are involved in following the Technology National Curriculum of which there are FOUR Key Stages.

You will find the work in this book especially useful for Key Stages 2 and 3, which cover the ages 9 to 14, and also give you a foundation for GCSE.

● You will be expected to study and achieve understanding of five Attainment Targets, which are:

   AT1 – Identifying needs and opportunities
   AT2 – Generating a design proposal
   AT3 – Planning and making
   AT4 – Evaluating
   AT5 – IT capability

● You will find that all the projects in this book meet these attainment targets but the level of study will change as you get older.

● You will be able to gain success at the attainment targets shown above, each of which has ten levels or stages within it, to show what you achieve.

● You will normally be expected to cover work between the range of level 2 to level 7 for each target, through using this book.

● The projects in this book are organised so that you can use them successfully at different levels, and also to suit your age.

● You should think of the ATs as a process through which you achieve something in technology.

● You may not always work through the ATs in the order given, for example you may evaluate something (AT4) and discover that you can make changes to improve its quality or performance.

● *AT5 – Information technology capability*

   The projects have not referred to this AT directly. However you will be expected to use any method that helps you achieve better results when you design and make. For example, the *Pen keeper* project could involve a survey of pens and pencils entered into a simple database, which would then produce a chart of results. The *Maze game* project could be planned and drawn out using a computer as an aid, allowing more choices and enabling you to make quicker changes to your design. In the *Wind-driven vehicle* project you could again use a database or graphics, e.g. for a test chart. You can also use software that illustrates a wide variety of simple mechanisms to help you with the fun board project. The *Light-barrier puzzle* uses simple technology. Parts could be designed with graphics and be plotted out by machines controlled by a computer. In the *Slotted structure* project, the design can be experimented with on a graphics system, allowing changes to be tried out.

   Using IT should be a familiar way of helping you to design something. The computer section shows you some simple starting points.

Pen keeper
This project gives the basic signposts to help you with designing and making.

AT1 from level 2 – a familiar context
AT2 from level 2 – develop a design proposal
AT3 from level 2 – working to a plan and using resources
AT4 from level 2 – appraisal of ideas (evaluating)

Wind-driven vehicle
AT1 from level 4 – investigate and gather information
AT2 from level 5 – record progress of ideas
AT3 from level 4 – overcome problems
AT4 from level 5 – justify the solution

Light-barrier puzzle
AT1 from level 5 – select a system
AT2 from level 6 – explore an idea
AT3 from level 5 – follow through to a solution
AT4 from level 6 – evaluate the methods used

Maze game
AT1 from level 3 – select relevant information
AT2 from level 4 – produce a realistic design
AT3 from level 4 – identify suitable materials
AT4 from level 3 – discuss process followed and result

Fun board
AT1 from level 5 – seek out and apply information
AT2 from level 5 – extend range of ideas
AT3 from level 5 – make use of a system
AT4 from level 5 – indicate possible improvements

Slotted structure
AT1 from level 3 – assess a suitable starting point
AT2 from level 5 – show various opportunities
AT3 from level 4 – be aware of different solutions
AT4 from level 5 – justify use of material

Design process

Design in practice

Design is about solving problems to meet a **need**. The need is usually described in a **design brief**. A design brief describes the problem that needs to be solved by your design. These examples show how an industrial designer has presented ideas and solved a problem.

The designer has to work within the limits of available components, manufacturing techniques, materials, costs and time.

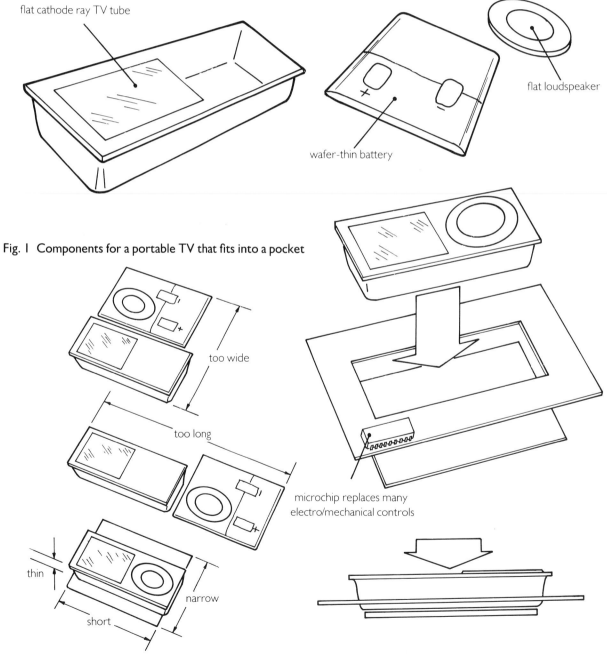

flat cathode ray TV tube

flat loudspeaker

wafer-thin battery

Fig. 1 Components for a portable TV that fits into a pocket

too wide

too long

thin

short

narrow

microchip replaces many electro/mechanical controls

Fig. 2 Arrangement of the components — it has to fit into a pocket!

Fig. 3 Better arrangement — keeps it thin

Completing the design

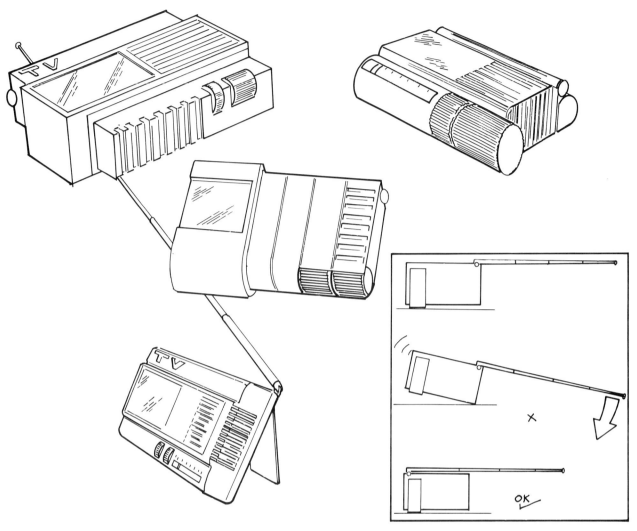

Fig. 4 Sketches of how the TV might look

Fig. 5 Stability of TV and aerial

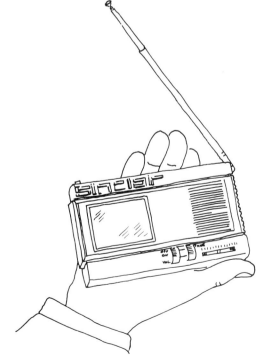

Fig. 6 Sinclair pocket TV

The pocket TV marketed by Sinclair Research has the following features:

● a shape and weight that fits easily into a pocket,
● simple rotary controls,
● an angled base and pull-out stand for viewing on a flat surface.

Things You Will Try

Try the design process yourself by imagining that you have the basic items in Fig. 1. You can now design your own pocket TV.

Portable microscope

Situation

Microscopes are widely used for medical and scientific purposes.

The designer has been asked to design a new portable microscope. The new design may be used by non-specialists for many different purposes.

Here we share the thoughts of the designer as he applies the design process.

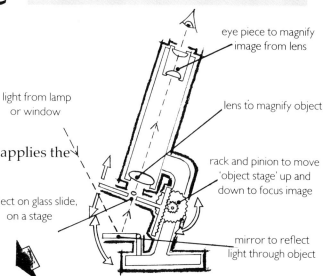

light from lamp or window

object on glass slide, on a stage

eye piece to magnify image from lens

lens to magnify object

rack and pinion to move 'object stage' up and down to focus image

mirror to reflect light through object

Fig. 7a Principles of the microscope

'To use bright daylight or a nearby lamp for lighting the object would be unreliable.'

'So I will add a light source with a built-in bulb, battery and switch.'

'To make the microscope small enough to fit into a pocket, I could change the shape of the light path. Make it more compact using two mirrors in a 'U' shape.'

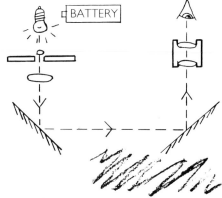

BATTERY

Fig. 7c Artificial light source

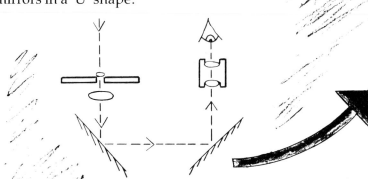

Fig. 7b Making the light path U-shaped

'I can now explore different shapes by considering the following:

- Many internal parts can be moved to different places, e.g. batteries, bulbs, mirrors.
- Comfort and the use to which the microscope will be put.
- How easy the controls are to identify and use.
- A shape that is exciting or interesting to look at.'

'Simply by drawing a "frame" around these parts I have the beginnings of a new design.'

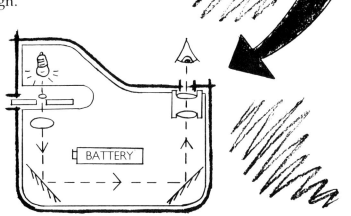

BATTERY

Fig. 7d Frame round parts of the pocket microscope

'To simplify the design I can move the lens to focus the object instead of moving the glass stage.'

Understanding the design

The more you *understand* about how things are made, and how they work, the more *control* you will have over the arrangement of the internal parts.

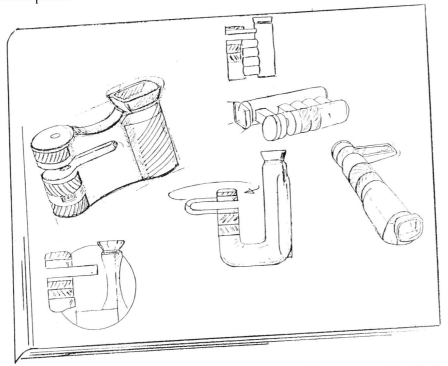

Fig. 8 Designer's sketch book page

Concept

Fig. 8 shows you how the idea or **concept** of a design can be explored through drawing.

Production

During the process of taking an idea through to a **finished product** there will be many changes.

A good way of showing the advantages of a new design is to make a realistic **model**. This helps a great deal in **evaluation** and **modifications.**

 Look at page 14 for other ideas about modelling, and the *Beginning to make* section, page 98, for ways in which you can use materials. The *Pen keeper* project, page 42, shows you how simple model making can help with a design.

Designers model and finished production version

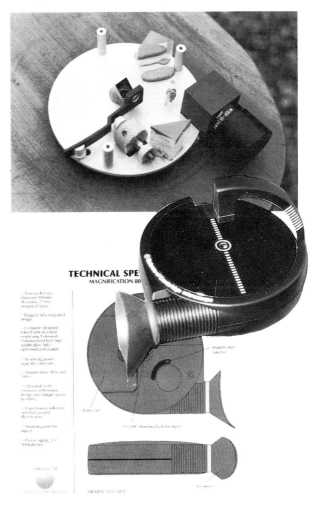

Things You Will Try

You can follow the process shown here to develop your own idea for a new microscope.

Approaching design

Why do we need design?

Fig. 9a Umpteem-decker bus hitting a bridge

Fig. 9b Telephone handset much too long

Fig. 9c Car with square wheels

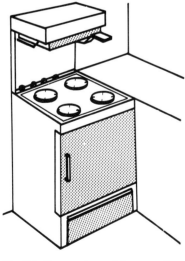

Fig. 9d Gas cooker with controls
badly placed

These obvious errors show that
design problems require planning

In the world we live in, we are often faced with problems that
could be solved if we thought about them carefully.

Where the solution to a problem involves designing and
making something, we call this the **design process**.

We expect good design to:

- avoid poor results by solving problems in
  advance.
- reduce the wastage of material, cost and
  time.
- make things pleasing to use and look at.
- solve the problem.

Design gives us a way of communicating by recording our
ideas, and it also helps us solve problems to meet a need.

Key words

Brief: a simple statement about a problem.
Analysis: breaking down a problem, so you can see how to
solve it.
Considerations: a simple list of points to consider.
Investigations: finding out and testing.
Research: finding relevant information.
Planning: thinking about and recording the order of doing
things.
Initial ideas: freehand sketches of your first ideas.
Best solution: choosing the best idea.
Modelling: a practical way of helping you understand designs
better.
Working drawing: a clear drawing from which you can make
the idea.
Making: putting your ideas into practice.
Modifications: changes made to improve the idea.
Evaluation: testing out the solution.

The design process

You can use this as a guide.

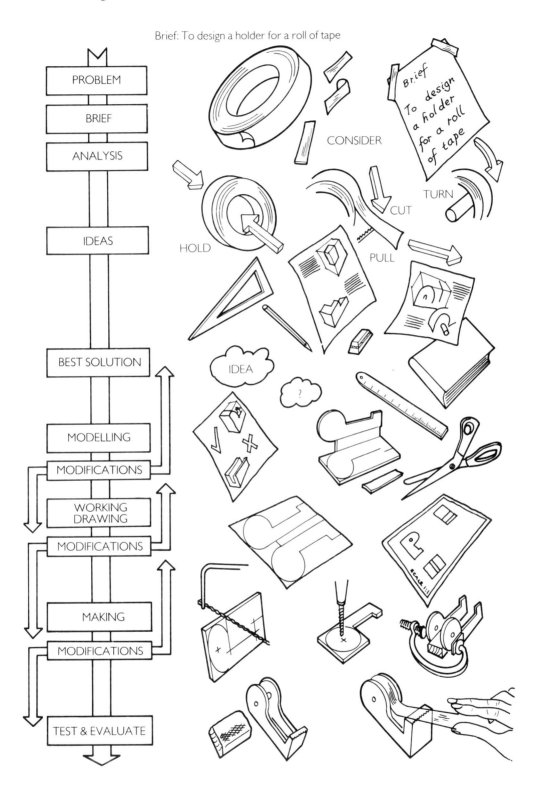

Fig. 10 Flow chart of design process

Applying the design process to a project

Nicola's design for a child's toy is an example of the design process. It shows some of the steps that you can use in design work. This is only a guide. *You* might use a different approach. It depends on the problem that you are solving.

A first stage

Write out for yourself the brief, limitations and considerations of the problem. Then sketch several initial ideas.

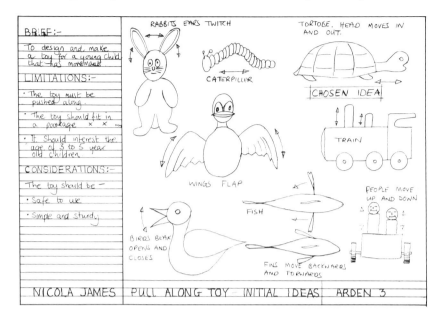

Fig. 11a First stage design ideas

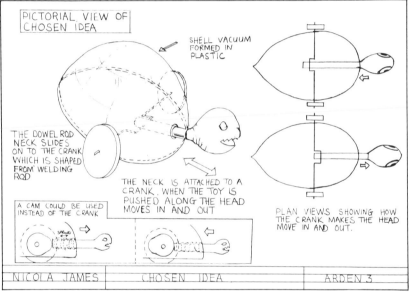

Fig.11b Further development of ideas

A middle stage

Choose one of your initial ideas to develop further. This will show greater detail, such as how it's put together.

Making a model at this stage is a way of helping you understand the idea better.

For help with modelling, see page 14.

Following this, you might need to make some modifications to your idea.

A final stage

A working drawing can be very helpful to you and others who look at your design. It can explain the exact appearance and size of the parts that make up your solution.

You may draw this freehand or with instruments.

This type of drawing usually shows two or more views of the idea.

An alternative to this would be an 'exploded parts' drawing — see page 30.

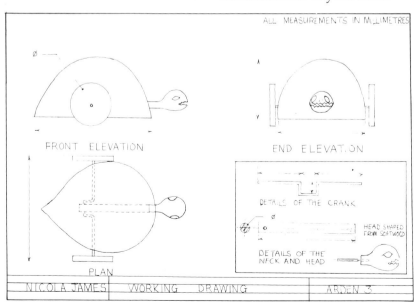

Fig. 11c Working drawing

Sources for design

You can find ideas for design from many different sources.

● Existing items can be used to develop a new design, e.g. you might think of a design for a clock by looking at clocks that are already produced.
● Natural sources, such as fruit, when examined in detail can inspire intricate work e.g. jewellery design.
● Other natural sources, e.g. animal bones, can inspire sculptural designs.

Fig. 12 Sources of ideas for design

Modelling an idea

Why make models?

Sometimes drawings can be difficult to understand on their own. A model can help you with an idea because it can be made directly in **three dimensions** (**3D**). If the size of the model is correct, or to scale, it will also help you to get the proportions right.

Fig. 13 Model of table tennis ball server

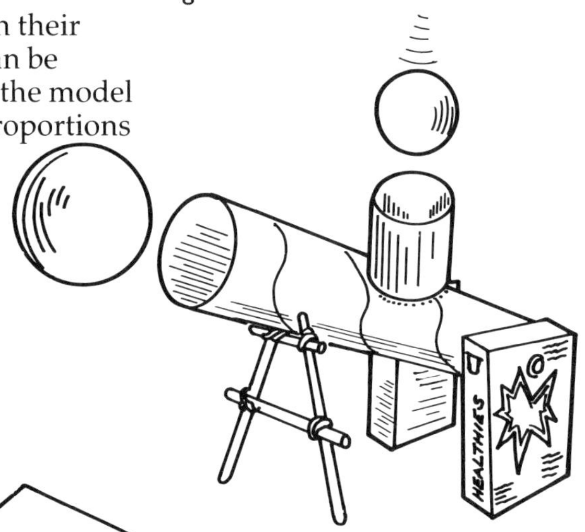

Modelling equipment and materials

You can use all sorts of materials to make models. A useful and easy-to-shape material is cardboard. Other choices are balsa wood, softwood, wire, polystyrene and thin plastic sheet.

Small and lightweight tools are the best ones for model making. Some useful items are shown in Fig. 15.

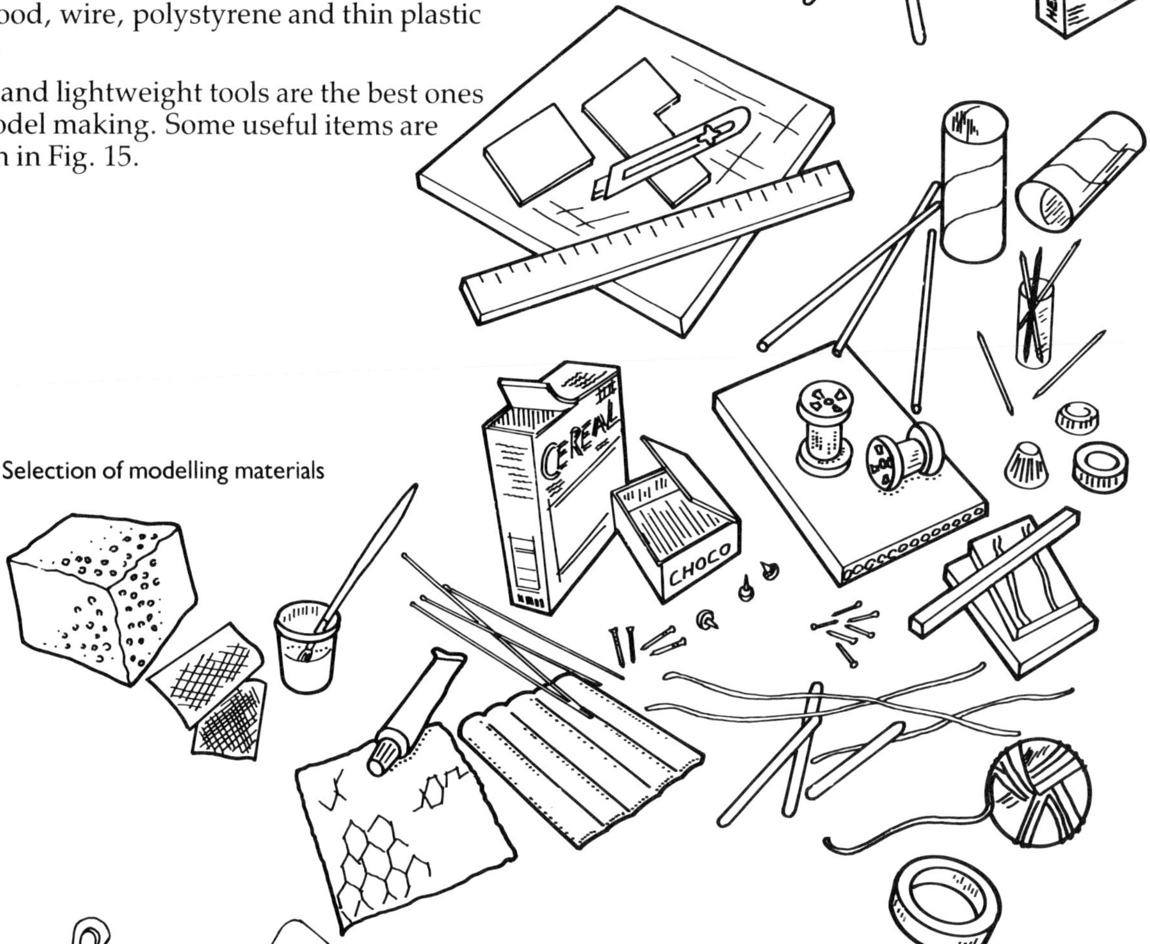

Fig. 14 Selection of modelling materials

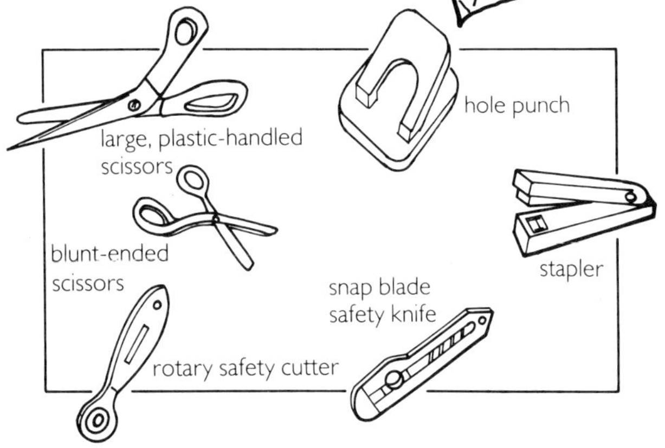

large, plastic-handled scissors

hole punch

blunt-ended scissors

stapler

snap blade safety knife

rotary safety cutter

Fig. 15 Useful tools for modelling

Safety

- Take care to follow safe practice with modelling equipment, as you would with regular making tools.
- For all cutting you should use safety-type tools, but you must keep your fingers clear of the cutting lines.

See Safety section — page 122.

Exploring shapes

Various shapes can be made by dividing up, cutting and re-joining the material.

This allows you to explore your idea in 3D.

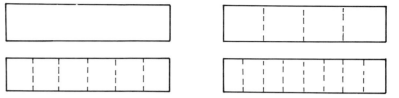

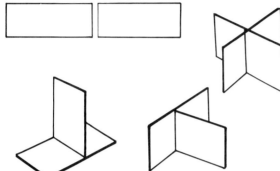

Fig. 16 Dividing and folding card

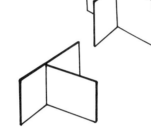
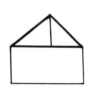

Fig. 17 Card cut in two

Fig. 18 Card cut in three

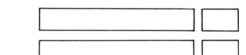

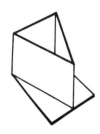
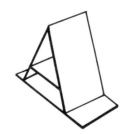

Fig. 19 Card cut in four

Fig. 20 Card cut in different sizes

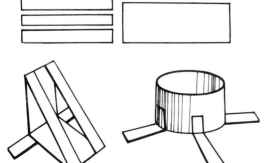

Fig. 21 Card cut in different proportions

Fig. 22 Different shapes

15

Projects by pupils

The projects that you do may need a different approach to the examples that you've just read about.

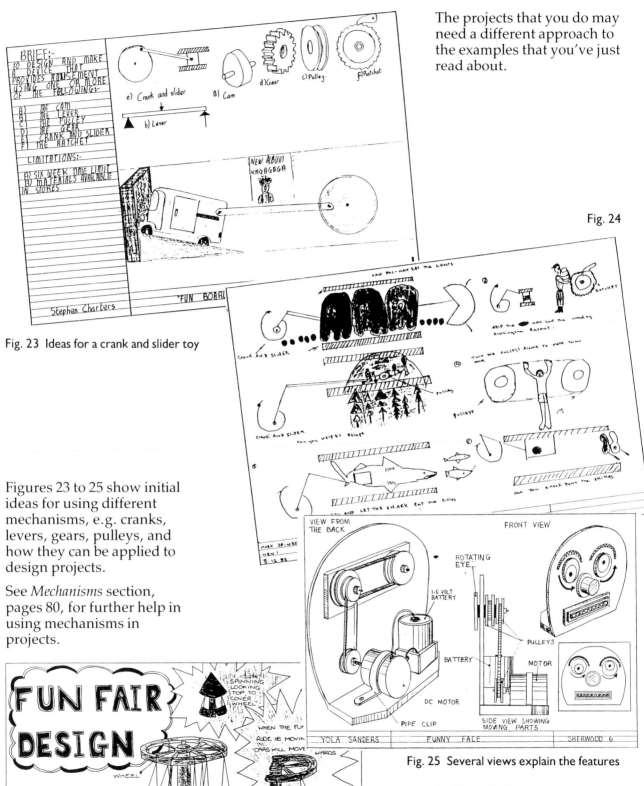

Fig. 24

Fig. 23 Ideas for a crank and slider toy

Figures 23 to 25 show initial ideas for using different mechanisms, e.g. cranks, levers, gears, pulleys, and how they can be applied to design projects.

See *Mechanisms* section, pages 80, for further help in using mechanisms in projects.

Fig. 25 Several views explain the features

In Fig. 25, the funny face, several views have been drawn to explain all the features of the project, i.e. front, side and back views.

In Fig. 26, the fun fair, parts of the design have been drawn in detail to show how it works.

Fig. 26 Parts of the design are drawn in enlarged detail

Things you will try

Now *you* can try out the design process.

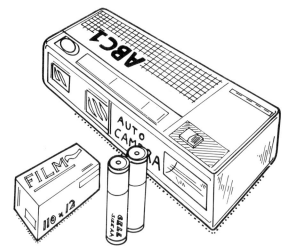

Fig. 27 Camera

Designing

1 A popular camera for taking on holiday is shown in Fig. 27. Design a protective case (made of clear plastic) to hold the camera, a film and batteries.

2 Design a small and simple light that can be easily fixed to any surface. You should be able to move the light to different positions.

Making

1 Design and make a holding device that will keep your hands free while you're using the telephone shown in Fig. 28. The shaded area shows where your holding device can be attached or fixed.

2 Design and make a dispenser to hold up to twenty small cooking-stock cubes. There must be a way of getting a cube out of the dispenser.

Fig. 28 Phone

Modelling

1 A manufacturer wishes to sell the six different pairs of scissors shown in Fig. 29. Design and model a simple packaging to hold and display them.

2 Design a simple container to carry a basic set of drawing equipment to and from school, and make a model of it.

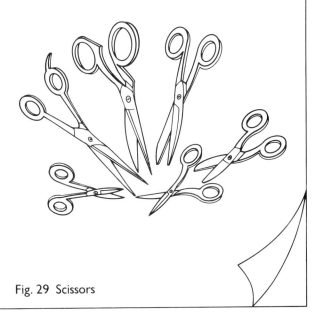

Fig. 29 Scissors

Resources

Why use resources?

This section is a guide to making good use of resources. You can use this as a further help when you are thinking about design problems.

Research and investigation

By doing some research and investigation you will have:

- a better understanding, before you start, of what is needed.
- an understanding of how other people tackle problems.
- an understanding, from other people, of what their needs are.
- found out what problems there might be, so that you can avoid them and produce a better final design.

Each project that you undertake will have different demands. Your investigation and research should help you to:

- discover the real need.
- decide which area you should work in, or find the problem.
- focus on the area that really interests you.
- satisfy the need.

Where to start?

Example problem

I want to design a holder for stationery
My holder will be for children of 6–9 years old
How do I start to investigate?

Fig. 1 Items of stationery

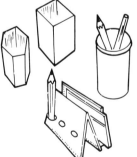

Fig. 2 Ideas for stationery holder

Fig. 3 Portable stationery holders

Consider: will your solution stay in one place or be portable?

Consider: some solutions only answer a part of the problem.
Look: for similar examples. Can you adapt an idea?

Consider: if portable, how will it be held? Will it be heavy? Evaluate and test.

> Remember, this is a necessary part of design thinking — it is a part of the DESIGN PROCESS.

How to use resources

Assemble and organise

You will need to *bring together* the information that you have found.

You may have:

- looked in books or magazines.
- written letters to ask for information.
- made notes or sketches.
- tried out things in an experimental way.

Locating information

For example, in a book you should:

- use the index to see if there is something about what you need.
- look at the chapter list to see if the book is relevant to the information you want.
- *not* just open the book randomly to look through.

Understanding the information

When you have found the information you want you should:

- read the relevant information carefully – you may need to take notes.
- make a note of the page number for future use.

A notebook or folder will be useful.

You may be able to cut out things you need from catalogues or magazines. These can be used on design sheets or in a folio.

Fig. 4 Flow chart: using resources

Fig. 5 Researching a problem

You should show how your *own* ideas develop from the sources used.

Break the problem down into smaller bits!

Where to find resources

Local environment — where you live

Sports centre

Library

Transport

Inside the home

Shopping centre

School

Design and make situation

Look around you for ideas

The room in which you work will have been designed to encourage you to be creative. Shown here are some resources you may use.

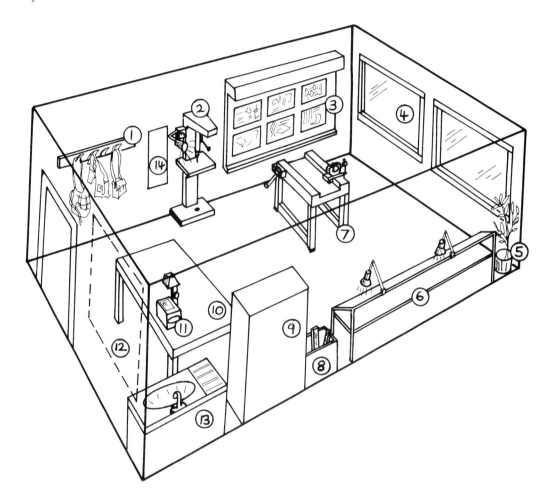

Fig. 6 3D view of a D & T room

Key
1 coats and bags storage
2 well-lit and guarded machines
3 display boards
4 natural light
5 natural resources
6 design area
7 multi-media benches
8 offcut box
9 tools/design materials cupboard
10 teacher's/discussion table
11 overhead projector
12 viewing screen/ blackboard/whiteboard
13 sink
14 clear safety signs

Use the room in which you work as a resource base.

Ask your teacher for help and guidance.

Things You Will Try

● Research and investigate the differences between various felt pens available in your local shops.
● Look through newspapers and magazines and make a collage of hi-fi systems, leisure wear or quiz games that appeal to young people.
● Choose one situation in the photographs opposite and list all the things you could investigate as an area for design.

 # Graphics for design

Graphic method

We use graphics to try to describe our ideas about things.

A **graphic method** is the technique we choose to use in our drawings.

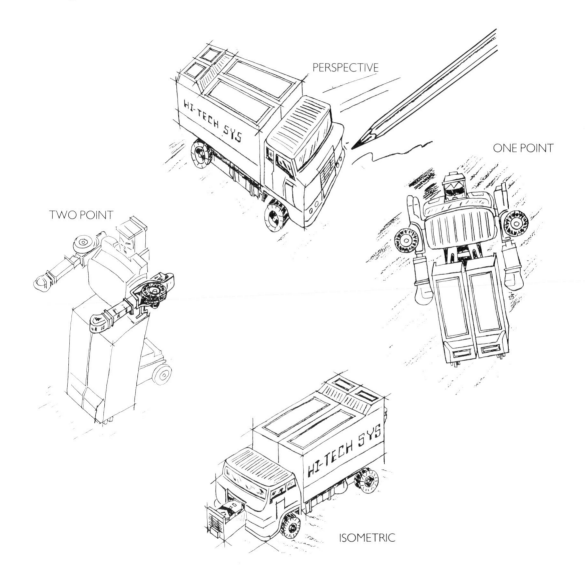

PERSPECTIVE

ONE POINT

TWO POINT

ISOMETRIC

Fig. I Transformer toy sketched in various 3D views

Just sketching something that you like many times will help you to practise your drawing skills.

Making your choice

You can use many different graphic methods for your design work. Some of them are explained in detail in this section. From these you can choose and develop your skills.

Look at the *Design process* section, page 6, for ideas about how you can organise your thoughts.

Freehand perspective is a very effective way of showing your basic design ideas.

Graphic process

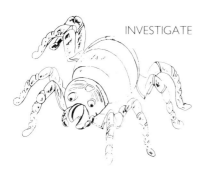

INVESTIGATE

underside mechanism

The graphic process is a way of *revealing* our ideas about the world in a visual way.

Fig. 2 Toy clockwork spider

Drawings can *investigate* objects to find out and show how things work.

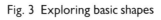

Fig. 3 Exploring basic shapes

EXPLORE

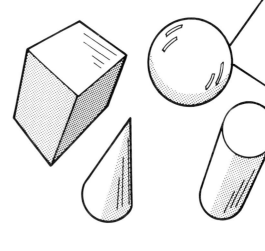

Drawing can *explain* in precise detail what a design is about.

Drawing can *explore* basic shapes to use in new forms.

EXPLAIN

AXONOMETRIC

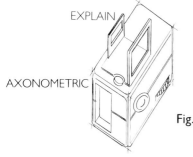

Fig. 4a Pocket camera

ORTHOGRAPHIC

Fig. 4b Orthographic transformer toy

Things You Will Try

- Choose one of your favourite possessions. Make drawings from different positions as you practise the different techniques shown on the next few pages.
- Use drawings in any style to investigate a mechanical item.
- Explore the basic shapes to produce packaging designs for a toiletry set.
- Use a detailed form of drawing to explain your first choice.

Beginning to draw

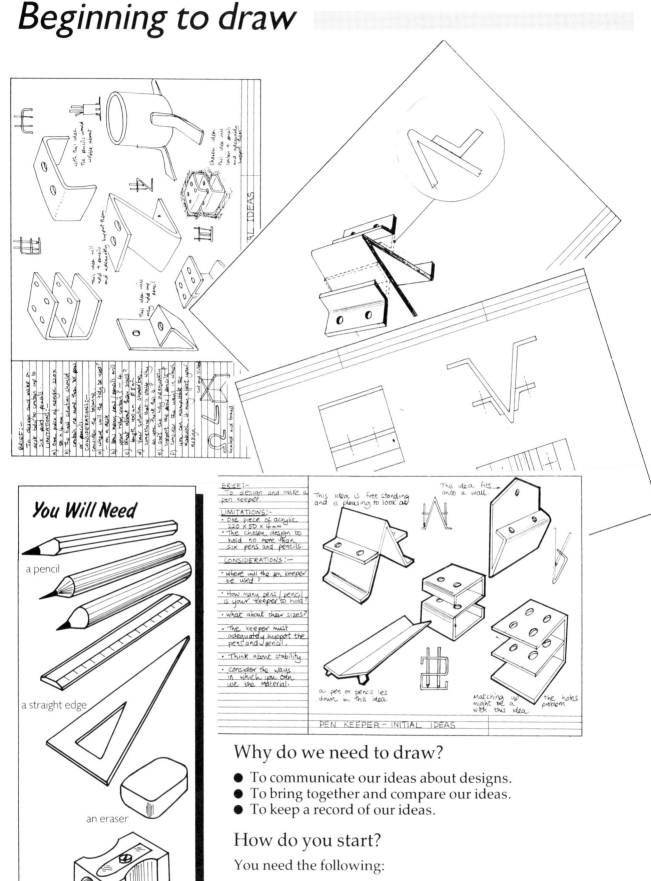

Fig. 5 Drawing tools

Why do we need to draw?

- To communicate our ideas about designs.
- To bring together and compare our ideas.
- To keep a record of our ideas.

How do you start?

You need the following:

- for simple drawing and sketching, an HB pencil.
- a pencil sharpener to keep a sharp point.
- an eraser for tidying up the the drawing.
- coloured pencils or pens to help make a particular idea stand out from the rest.
- a ruler or set square can be used later for detailed drawings.

A first step

Holding the pencil

CHECK: Is your pencil sharp?

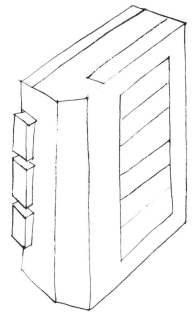

Fig. 6 How not to hold a pencil

If you bunch your fingers around the pencil, you may not find it so easy to sketch freely — see Fig. 6.

Fig. 7 How to hold a pencil

Holding the pencil away from the point and relaxing your fingers helps you use the wrist freely — see Fig. 7. By holding the pencil this way you should find sketching easier.

Freehand sketching

Freehand lines can be vertical, horizontal or angled — see Fig. 8.

Fig. 9 A simple line drawing

Fig. 8 Drawing lines

Try to avoid short, jerky movements and going back over a line.

Fig. 10 Different types of lines used in drawings

SECOND   FLOOR

Things You Will Try

● Practise drawing freehand lines, keeping them a regular distance apart.
● Sketch three or four objects that you can see around you using freehand lines.
● Collect examples of drawings that show different types and quality of lines.

25

Perspective

Perspective is a way of making drawings look very realistic. It can make it clear to someone what your design is about.

There are two main methods:

● one-point perspective drawing, which has one **vanishing point**.
● two-point perspective drawing, which has two vanishing points.

Guide: These stages show you a general method for one-point perspective

● Draw a line for the **horizon** and mark a cross for one vanishing point (1).
● For a simple box, the front is a square (2).
● Draw lines to the vanishing point (3).
● Draw the top and one side (4).
● Try a more complicated shape (5).

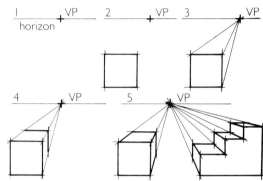

> Remember, keep all your construction lines feint because they are only a guide.

Fig. 11 One point perspective drawing

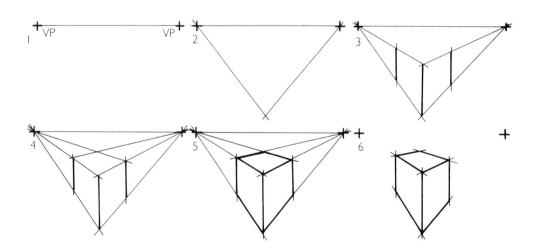

Fig. 12 Two point perspective drawing

Things You Will Try

● Using one-point perspective, draw a simple table and chair.
● Complete your drawing by adding the features of a modern living room.
● Using two-point perspective, design a house of the future or a future transport vehicle.

Choosing the viewpoint

Sketching in perspective will take practice.
The drawing will change in appearance,
depending on where you place the vanishing
points and the distance that you make the
object from the horizon.

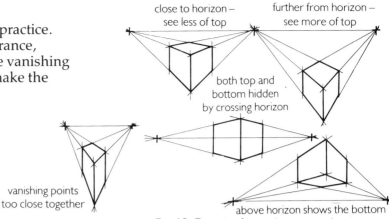

close to horizon –
see less of top

further from horizon –
see more of top

both top and
bottom hidden
by crossing horizon

vanishing points
too close together

above horizon shows the bottom

Fig. 13 Drawing boxes in perspective

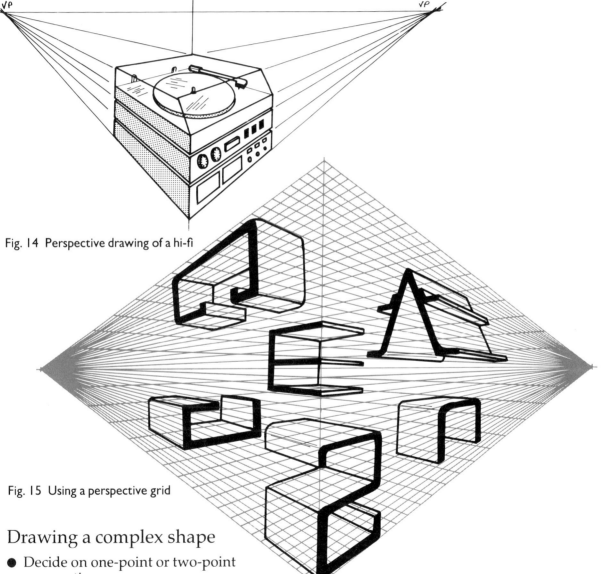

vp   vp

Fig. 14 Perspective drawing of a hi-fi

Fig. 15 Using a perspective grid

Drawing a complex shape

- Decide on one-point or two-point perspective.
- Choose a viewpoint.
- Sketch a box you can draw the object in.
- Ask yourself is the object short, tall, fat or thin?
- Draw in the features, but remember to keep the lines going to the vanishing points.
- If you find it difficult to draw in this way then you can use a perspective grid to guide you — see Fig. 15.

Things You Will Try

Try drawing boxes to different vanishing points.

27

Axonometrics

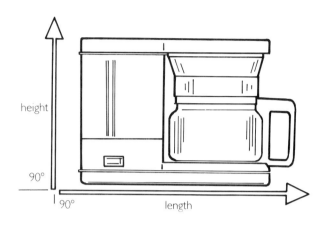

Axonometric drawing is a way of making an object look three-dimensional (3D). The length, height and depth are shown, but not in perspective. Instead the three faces are angled to give a 3D impression.

Usually:

- drawings with 30° angles are known as **isometric**.
- drawings with 45° angles are called **axonometric**.
- drawings with 30° and 60° angles are called **planometric**.

With axonometric and planometric drawings the heights may be reduced by one-third. This stops the objects from looking taller than they should.

Fig. 16 2D orthographic view of a coffee maker

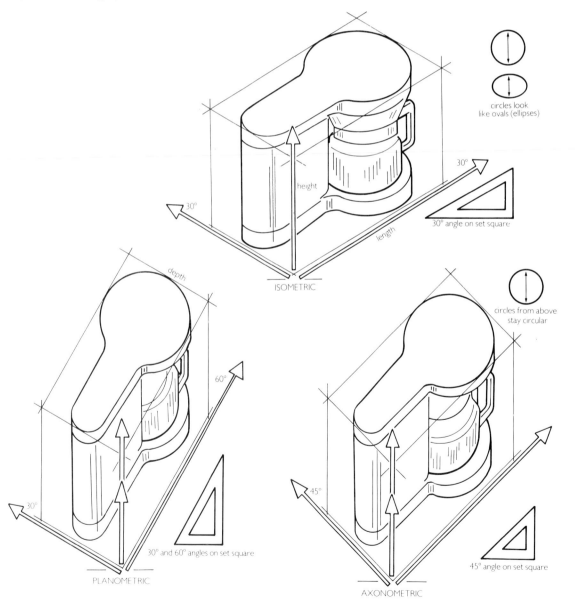

Fig. 17 Different views drawn in isometric, planometric and axonometric

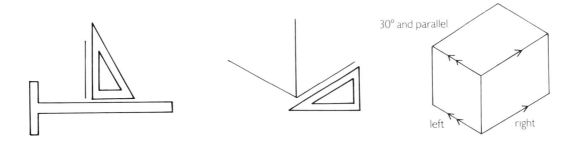

Fig. 18 Drawing in isometric

Isometric: a simple method

- Verticals stay vertical.
- Sides are angled at 30° left and right.
- Lines are drawn at 30° and parallel.

Another 3D method is **oblique**.

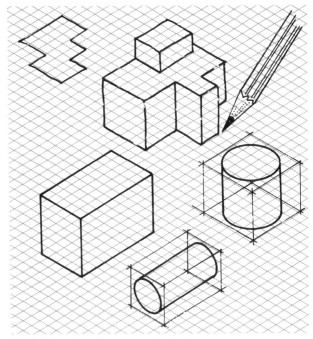

Fig. 19 Drawing on isometric grid paper

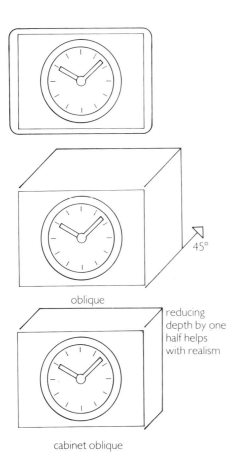

oblique

reducing
depth by one
half helps
with realism

45°

cabinet oblique

Fig. 20 Different views drawn in oblique

Axonometrics usually help with drawing
difficult shapes like circles.

When to use axonometrics

Axonometrics are a geometrical way of giving
a 3D view.

They are useful because you can measure the
length, height and depth directly on the
drawing.

You can use various aids to help you achieve
an accurate drawing, such as grids, set-
squares, etc.

Things You Will Try

- Make freehand perspective and
  axonometric sketches of familiar objects.
  Compare their 'realism'.
- Make an accurate measured drawing of a
  clock in isometric and oblique.

Exploded drawing

Why use an exploded drawing?

Many of the drawing methods shown, such as perspective and axonometrics, help to explain the appearance of an object.

An exploded drawing helps to show all the parts that make up an object. This gives you a clear idea of how the object is put together.

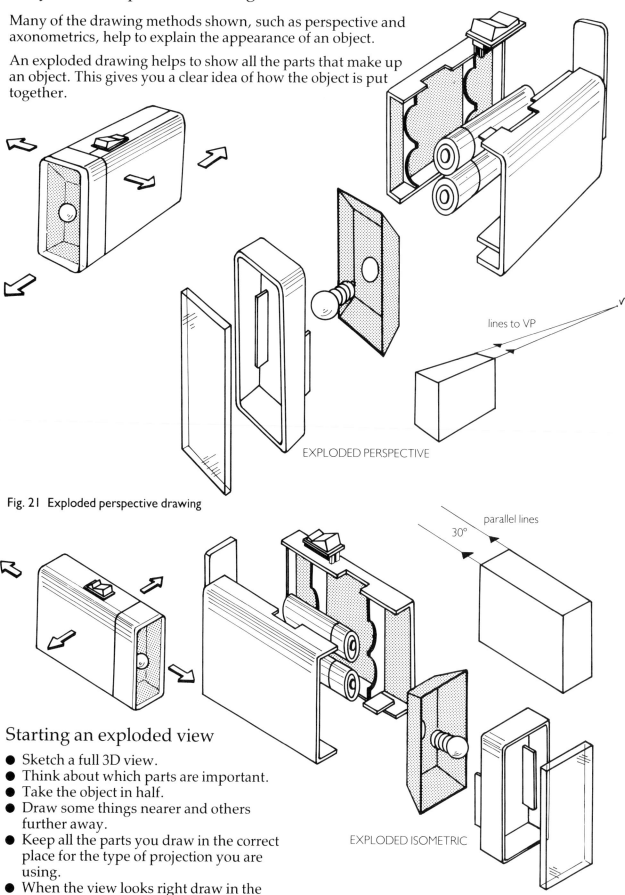

EXPLODED PERSPECTIVE

Fig. 21 Exploded perspective drawing

EXPLODED ISOMETRIC

Starting an exploded view

● Sketch a full 3D view.
● Think about which parts are important.
● Take the object in half.
● Draw some things nearer and others further away.
● Keep all the parts you draw in the correct place for the type of projection you are using.
● When the view looks right draw in the detail.

Fig. 22 Exploded isometric drawing

Sequence drawing

This type of drawing is useful to show graphically a *step-by-step* sequence of how something is made or put together.

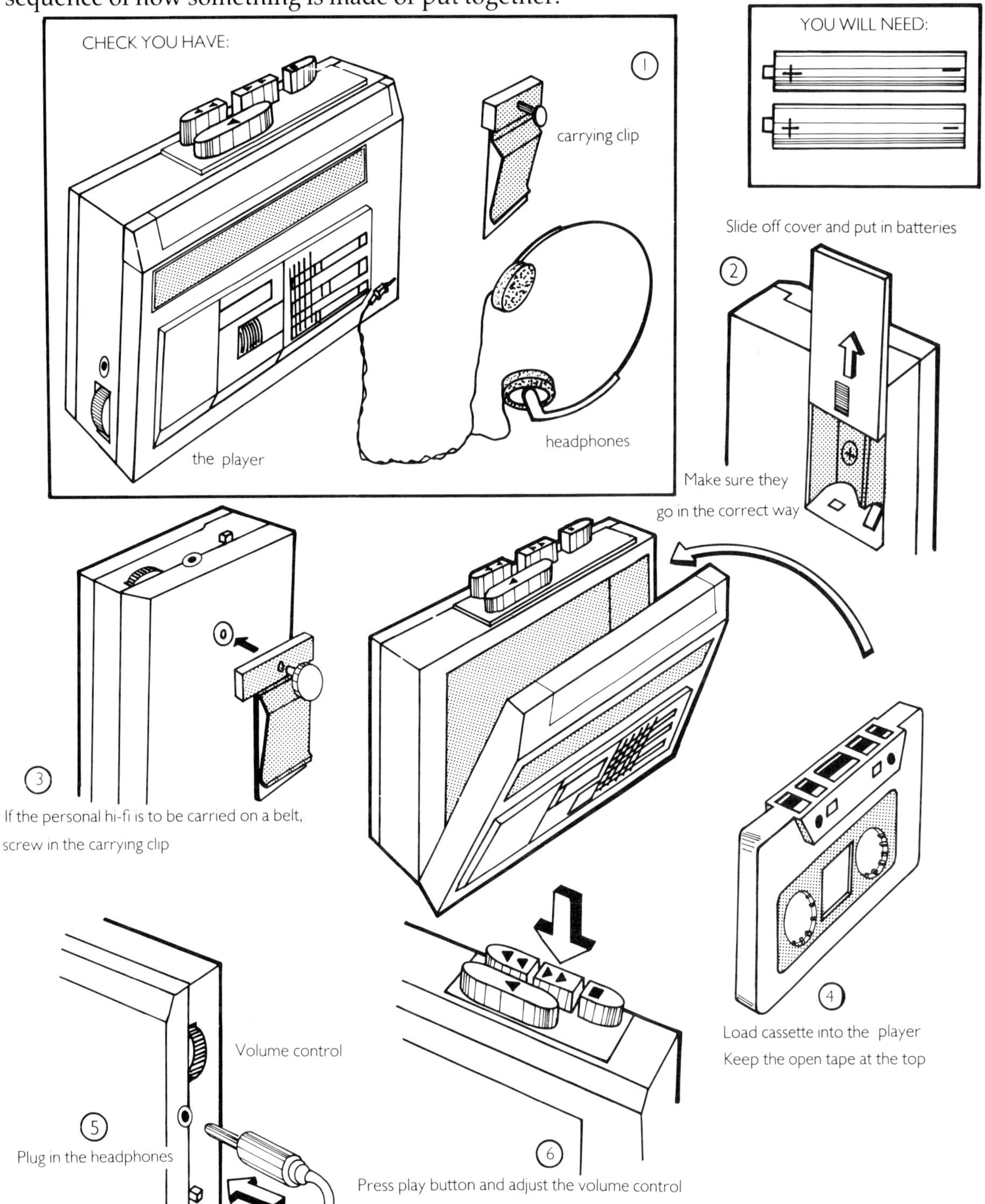

CHECK YOU HAVE:

carrying clip

headphones

the player

①

YOU WILL NEED:

②

Slide off cover and put in batteries

Make sure they go in the correct way

③

If the personal hi-fi is to be carried on a belt, screw in the carrying clip

④

Load cassette into the player
Keep the open tape at the top

Volume control

⑤

Plug in the headphones

⑥

Press play button and adjust the volume control

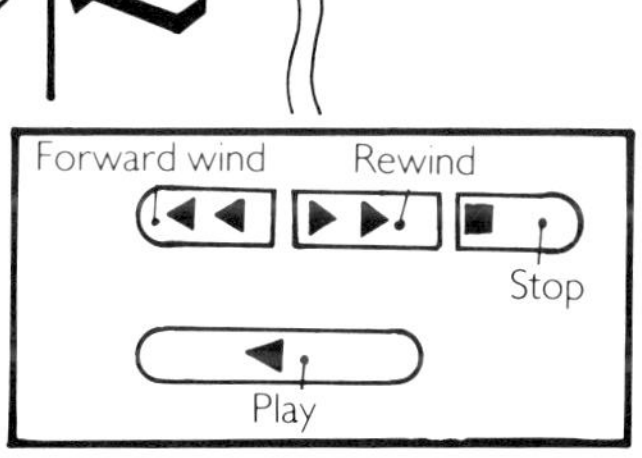

Forward wind   Rewind

Stop

Play

Things You Will Try

● Choose a simple but interesting object that you know about and make an exploded drawing in either perspective or isometric.
● Prepare a sequence drawing to show how you make a cup of tea or coffee.

Fig. 23 A sequence for operating a personal hi-fi

Working drawings — orthographic

Orthographic drawings are a **system** of technical drawings. They are flat 2D drawings that show the exact details of an object.

They are arranged in a special way called **projections**. There are two types: third-angle and first angle projections. If you look carefully at both types of projection you will see that the 2D views are in fact the same, but they are arranged in different positions.

Each of the views has a particular name, but often all orthographic drawings are called 'plans'. This means they are exact enough to work from to make the object. Measurements and a scale are used, for example, full size (1:1) — see 'Working to scale', page 33.

How to draw in third-angle projection

The 3D perspective view (Fig. 24) shows a realistic impression of a hairdryer. From this drawing you can recognise it as a hairdryer.

Fig. 24 Hairdryer

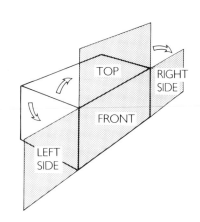

Imagine that the hairdryer is contained in a transparent box. If you look at the hairdryer straight on from different positions you will see different 2D views. Imagine each view is drawn or *projected* on the wall of the box nearest you as you look at that view. Now imagine that the box is opened out flat (Fig. 25). This shows you how the different 2D views are arranged in the third-angle projection drawing (Fig. 26).

Fig. 25 'Transparent box' for third angle projection

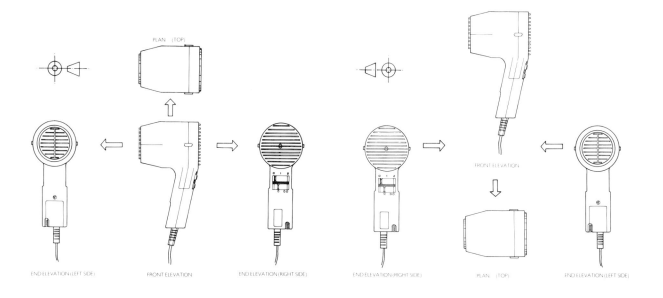

Fig. 26 Third angle orthographic projection

Fig. 27 First angle orthographic projection

How to draw in first-angle projection

The 3D perspective view (Fig. 28) shows a realistic impression of the hairdryer. Imagine the hairdryer inside a box, as you did for the third-angle projection. Look at the hairdryer straight on from the different positions shown. This time, imagine the 2D views projected on the *inside* faces of the box, behind the hairdryer. Opening the box out flat (Fig. 29) gives the arrangement of the parts of the first-angle projection (Fig. 27).

Working to scale

To be exact, an orthographic drawing must be *to scale*. 3D drawings show you exactly what objects look like, but you can't be sure how big they really are.

A scale will state the exact size. Often full-size or half-full size scales are used, but with larger objects a ratio is used, for example, 1 to 10 (1:10). This would mean one unit on the drawing equals ten units on the real object.

This will also mean that you can draw to a size that is convenient for the paper you have chosen.

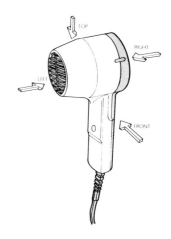

Fig. 28 Hairdryer

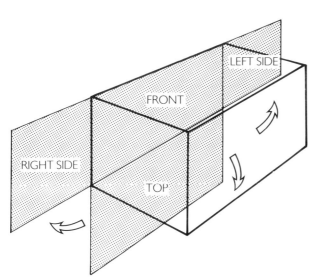

Fig. 29 'Transparent box' for first angle projection

Measurements

Sizes or **dimensions** are placed on the drawing in a certain way. They are shown by arrows drawn between **limit lines**.

Note that:

- limit lines have a small gap between them and the drawing
- draw neat, sharp arrowheads
- dimension figures are *above* the dimension lines.

Third-angle rule: project views forward

First-angle rule: project views through

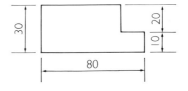

Fig. 30 Dimensioning

33

Rendering

Rendering is a word used to describe how a drawing is made to look realistic. You do not need to use expensive equipment to achieve a good rendering. Here, low-cost colour pencils and felt-tipped pens have been used to show you what can be done.

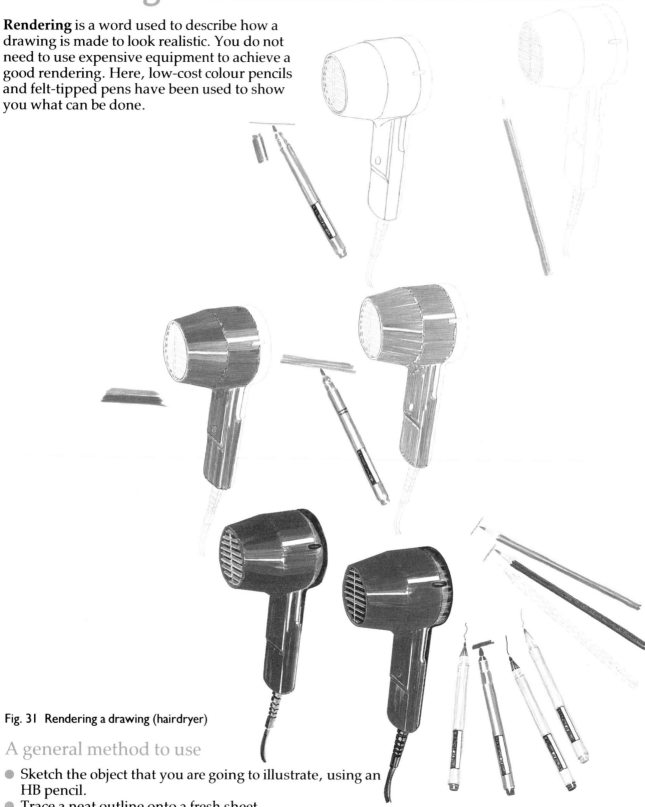

Fig. 31 Rendering a drawing (hairdryer)

A general method to use

- Sketch the object that you are going to illustrate, using an HB pencil.
- Trace a neat outline onto a fresh sheet.
- Use a light colour to outline the drawing.
- Use bold strokes to shade the drawing. Follow the shape and leave some highlights in white.
- Going over a *second time* in the same colour can add a deeper tone.
- A white pencil can be used to 'put back' light, if the highlights have been missed.
- Colour pencils can be used to tidy up details.

2D views like orthographics can also be rendered.

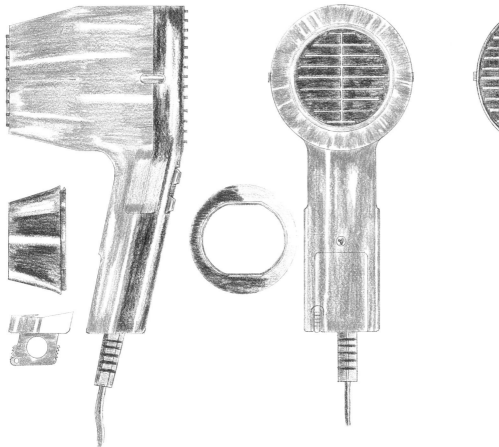
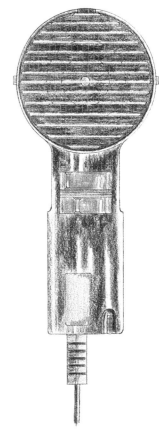

Fig. 32 Drawings rendered in coloured pencil

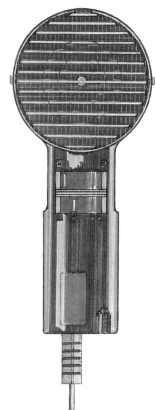

Fig. 33 Drawings rendered in felt pen

Applying colour — the theory

Using colour on your design drawings can improve the *presentation* or help to make the drawings look *real*.
Yet it is easy to spoil a drawing by using colour badly. Here you will find a guide to colour that will help you when you are making a choice.

Primary colours

These are the three basic colours — red, yellow and blue.

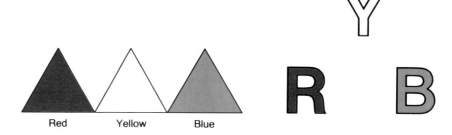

Fig. 34 Primary colours

Secondary colours

These are the three basic colour mixtures of the primary colours — orange, green and violet.

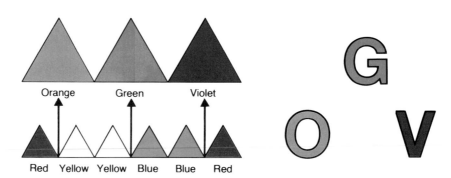

Fig. 35 Secondary colours

Tertiary colours

These are the three basic sets of colours that are mixtures of a primary colour and a secondary colour — deep orange, pale orange, leaf green (pale), emerald green (deep), purple and indigo.

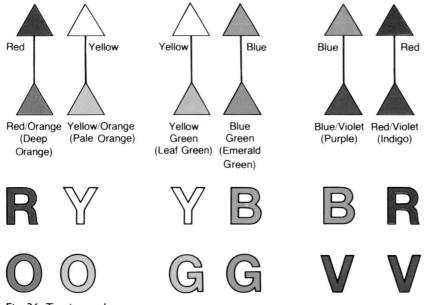

Fig. 36 Tertiary colours

Primary and secondary colours

When the colours are arranged as shown, you can see which colours **harmonise** and which **contrast**.
The primary colours *harmonise* with the tertiary colours, but *contrast* with the secondary colours.

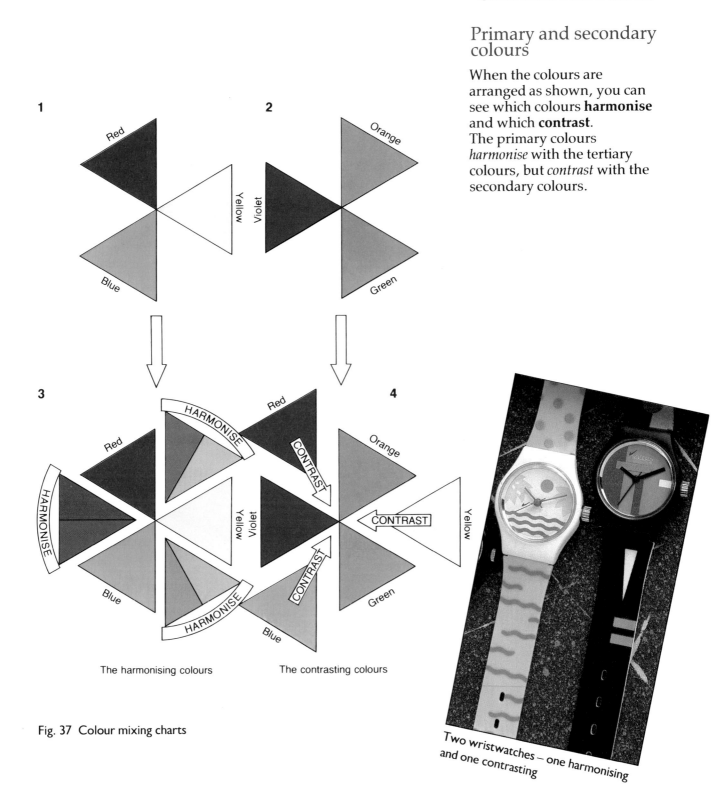

Fig. 37 Colour mixing charts

Two wristwatches – one harmonising and one contrasting

How to use the charts

- To mix the colour orange on chart 2 you look for the gap on chart 1 between red and yellow. This is where orange would be if both charts 1 and 2 were joined. So orange is made by mixing red and yellow.
- Try this with green and violet.
- To choose a harmonising colour for a primary colour look at chart 3.
- To choose a contrasting colour look at chart 4. For example, red and green are colours that clash. So it is better to avoid this colour combination, unless it is for a special effect.

Applying colour — the practice

You can use a variety of
different ways to achieve a
good rendering.

Manufactured articles

Often colour and texture are
bright and contrasting in
manufactured articles. When
natural materials are used
they often blend and
harmonise.

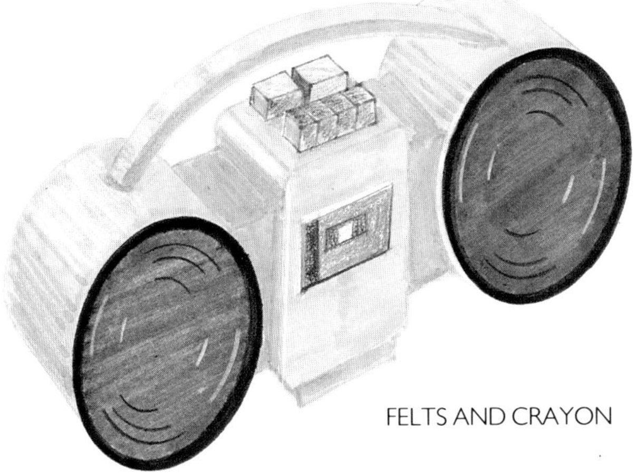

FELTS AND CRAYON

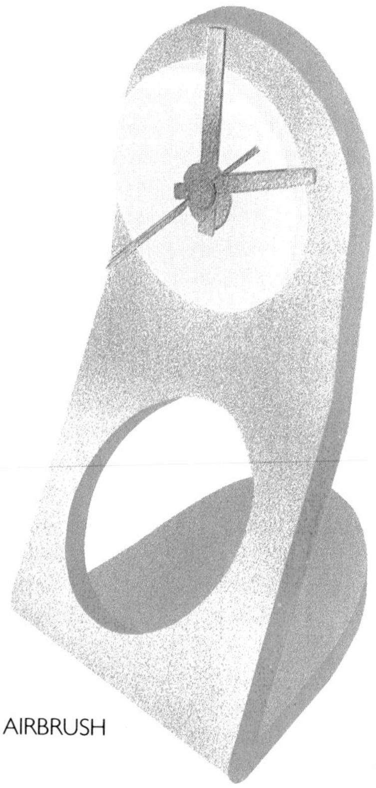

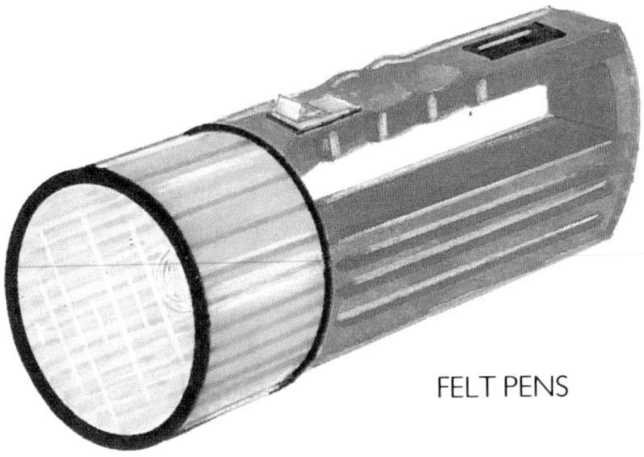

FELT PENS

AIRBRUSH

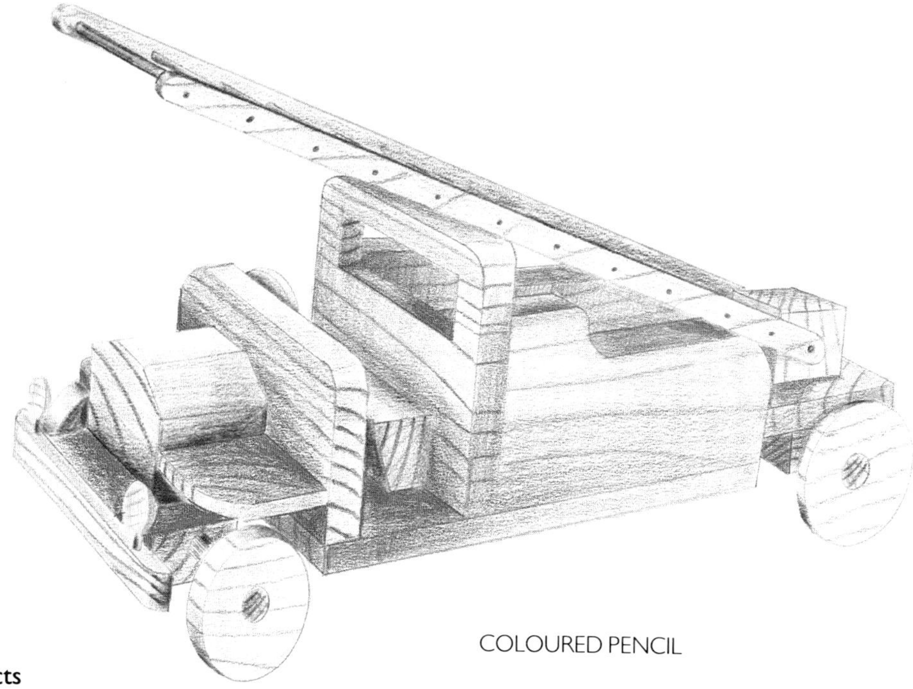

COLOURED PENCIL

Fig. 38 Drawings of made objects

Natural sources

When you look at and investigate natural things, you will see that colour and texture is often very varied and yet harmonious.

CHALK AND CRAYON

PASTELS

WATERCOLOUR

INKS

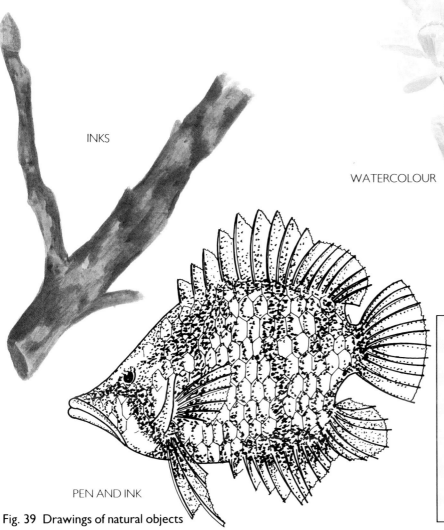

PEN AND INK

Fig. 39 Drawings of natural objects

Things You Will Try

- With all graphics you should experiment to find the technique that suits you best.
- You may wish to mix different methods, for example, felt-tip pen and colour pencils.

Presenting your drawings

Well-presented drawings can make our ideas better understood. They are more appealing to look at.

Here are some ways in which you can improve the presentation of your work.

Fig. 40 Presenting design drawings

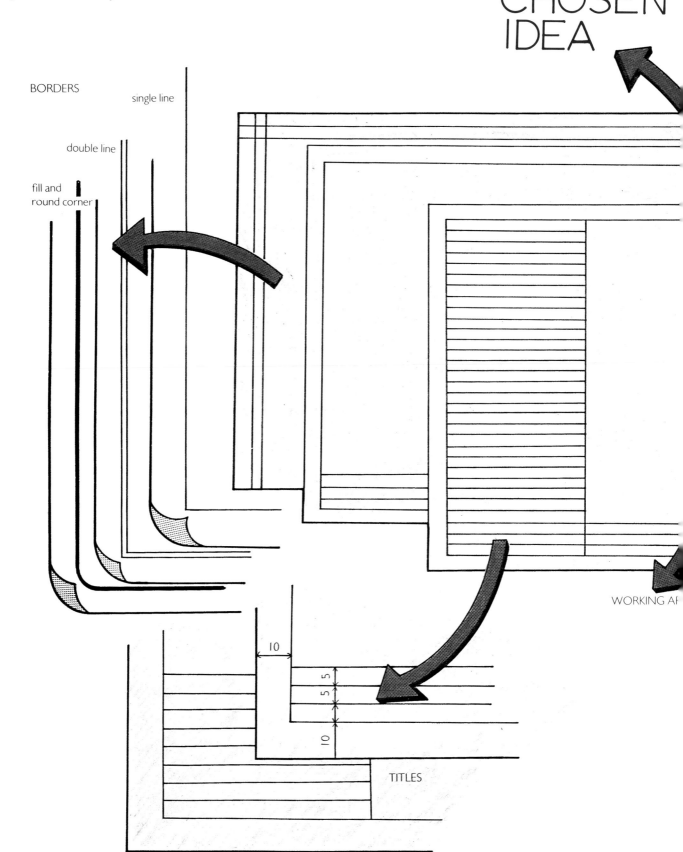

HEADING/SHEET NUMBER

CHOSEN IDEA

BORDERS

single line

double line

fill and round corner

WORKING AREA

10

5 5

10

TITLES

LOGO

PRINTING

use guidelines

rub off letters

stencils

LETTERING

Pen keeper

This project gives the basic signposts for designing and making.

The problem

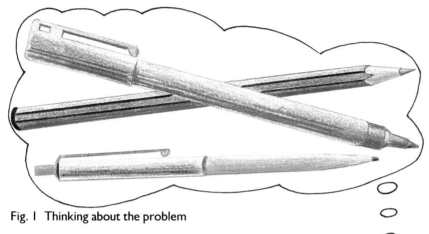

Fig. 1 Thinking about the problem

The brief

To design and make a pen keeper.

We often lose pens and pencils. If we have something that will keep them all together then they will be easy to find.

Fig. 2

Limitations

● You can use one piece of acrylic.
● Your chosen design must hold up to six pens or pencils.

Considerations

You will need to think about the following points for your design.

Where would a pen keeper be useful?

By the telephone

On the desk

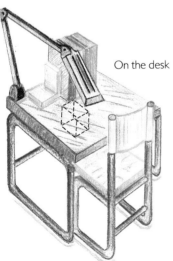

Fig. 3 Places where your pen keeper might be used

How many pens or pencils will your keeper contain?

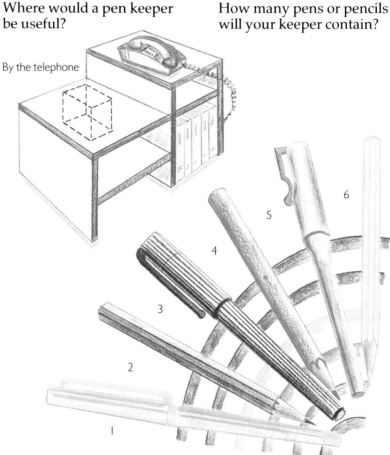

Fig. 4 Six pens/pencils

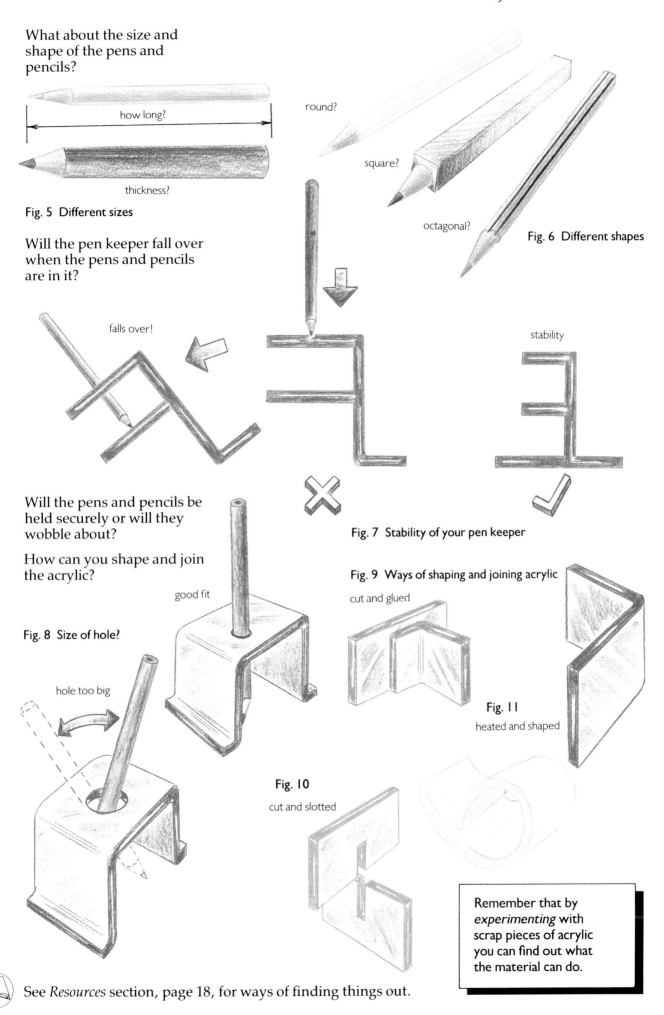

What about the size and shape of the pens and pencils?

how long?

thickness?

Fig. 5 Different sizes

round?

square?

octagonal?

Fig. 6 Different shapes

Will the pen keeper fall over when the pens and pencils are in it?

falls over!

stability

Fig. 7 Stability of your pen keeper

Will the pens and pencils be held securely or will they wobble about?

How can you shape and join the acrylic?

good fit

Fig. 8 Size of hole?

hole too big

Fig. 9 Ways of shaping and joining acrylic

cut and glued

Fig. 11
heated and shaped

Fig. 10
cut and slotted

Remember that by *experimenting* with scrap pieces of acrylic you can find out what the material can do.

See *Resources* section, page 18, for ways of finding things out.

Designing

These drawings show you how you could begin to design your pen keeper. The ideas have been drawn in 3D to show how effective this can be.

See pages 6–17 for help with the design process.

Remember to draw *your own* designs and do not copy these examples. They are not the only answer to the problem.

There will be no clearly right or wrong answers, but some may be better than others.

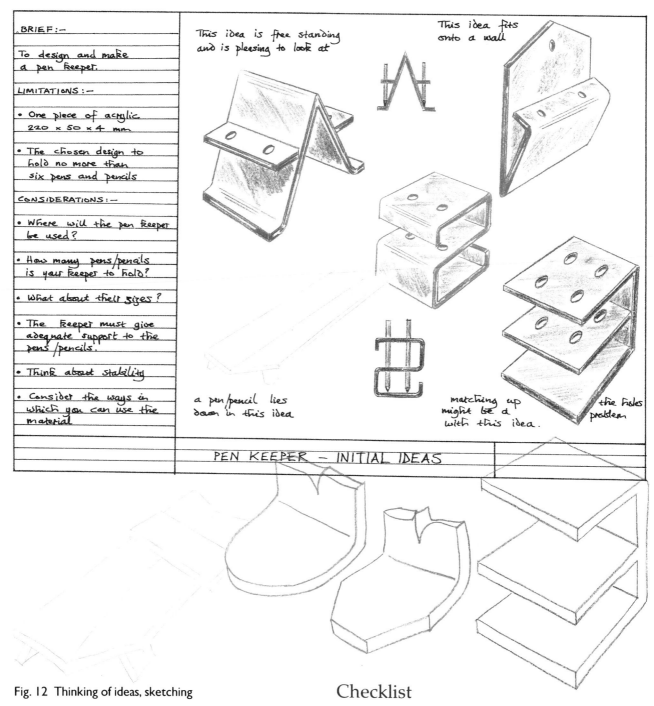

BRIEF:—

To design and make a pen keeper.

LIMITATIONS:—

• One piece of acrylic 220 × 50 × 4 mm

• The chosen design to hold no more than six pens and pencils

CONSIDERATIONS:—

• Where will the pen keeper be used?

• How many pens/pencils is your keeper to hold?

• What about their sizes?

• The keeper must give adequate support to the pens/pencils.

• Think about stability

• Consider the ways in which you can use the material

This idea is free standing and is pleasing to look at

This idea fits onto a wall

a pen/pencil lies down in this idea

matching up might be d with this idea.

the holes problem

PEN KEEPER — INITIAL IDEAS

Fig. 12 Thinking of ideas, sketching

Checklist

● Set out a design sheet like the one above.
● Write out for yourself the brief, the limitations and the considerations.
● Draw *freehand* three or four initial ideas.

Understanding the design better

Modelling the idea

You may find it easier to model your idea in a material like cardboard. It will help you to work out sizes, especially for your chosen idea.

See page 14 for further help with modelling.

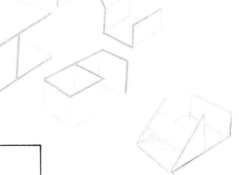

Fig. 13 Some ideas modelled in card

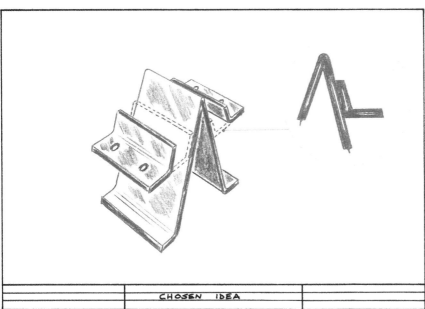

CHOSEN IDEA

Fig. 14 3D drawing of chosen idea

Completing your design

From the **initial designs** choose the one that you like best and which you think works well.

Draw out your **chosen idea.** This should be a 3D drawing that shows some detail. See page 22 for help with graphics.

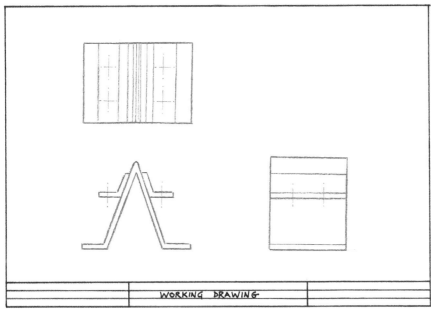

WORKING DRAWING

Fig. 15 Working drawing

Working drawing

A working drawing is useful to show the proportions and measurements of your design. This may be done freehand or using instruments.

If you have made a model you can take measurements from it directly.

Colour and clear labelling can be used to make your drawings easier to follow.

See pages 34–39 for help with colour.

Making the project

Whatever design you choose, here are some important points to help you make it from acrylic.

1 Smoothing the edges

Step 1. 'Crossfile' and 'drawfile' the edges.
Step 2. Using 'wet or dry' paper improves the finish. For more help see *Beginning to make* page 121.

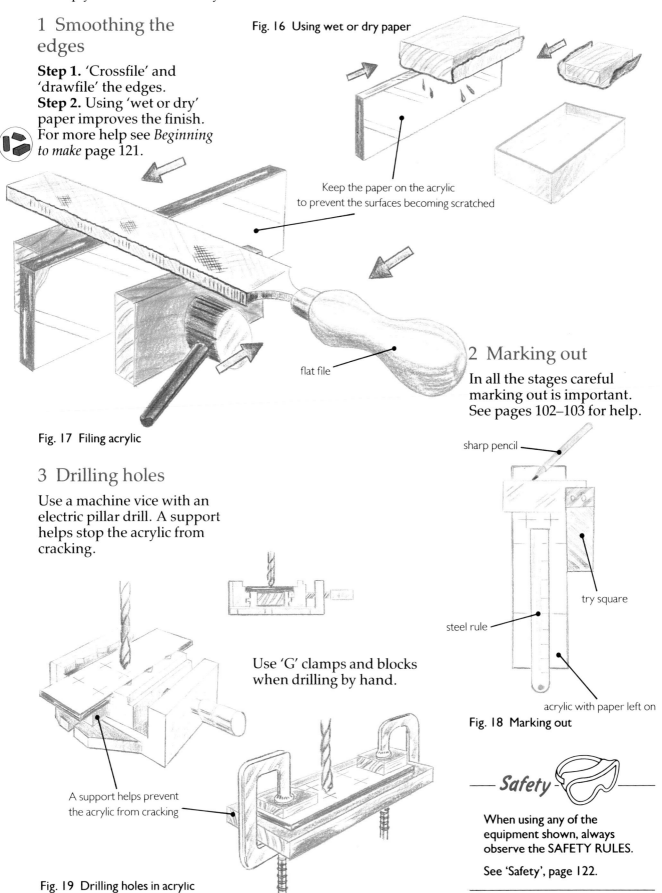

Fig. 16 Using wet or dry paper

Keep the paper on the acrylic to prevent the surfaces becoming scratched

flat file

Fig. 17 Filing acrylic

2 Marking out

In all the stages careful marking out is important. See pages 102–103 for help.

sharp pencil

try square

steel rule

acrylic with paper left on

Fig. 18 Marking out

3 Drilling holes

Use a machine vice with an electric pillar drill. A support helps stop the acrylic from cracking.

Use 'G' clamps and blocks when drilling by hand.

A support helps prevent the acrylic from cracking

Fig. 19 Drilling holes in acrylic

— **Safety** —

When using any of the equipment shown, always observe the SAFETY RULES.

See 'Safety', page 122.

4 Shaping and finishing

A round file helps to smooth any burrs left by drilling.

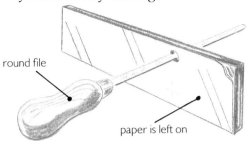

round file

paper is left on

Fig. 20 Smoothing holes

5 Forming the acrylic

The acrylic will need to be heated evenly to soften it enough to shape easily. An oven or line bender will allow you to control the heating.

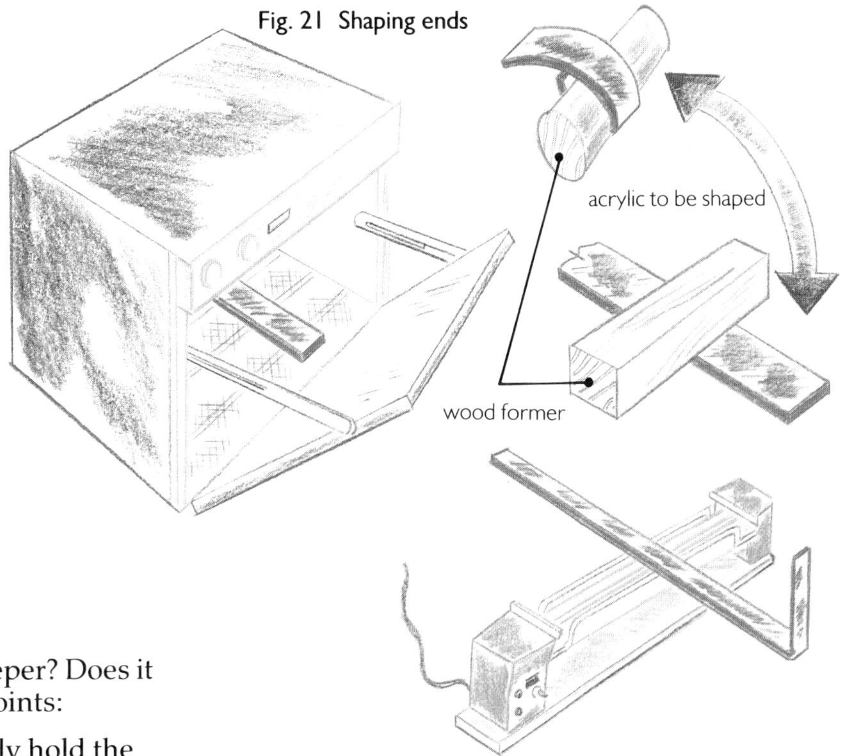

6 Sticking and holding together

Your design may have parts that need to be stuck together. For help see *Beginning to make*/assembling the material, page 111.

Evaluation

How successful is your pen keeper? Does it satisfy some of the following points:

- Does your design successfully hold the pens?
- Is it stable with the pens in place or does it fall over?
- Is it easy to use?
- Does it make good use of the acrylic?
- Is it attractive and well finished?
- Ask your friends for their opinions of your pen keeper.

Acrylic or metal polish can be used for a final finish.

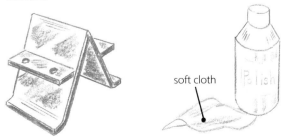

soft cloth

Fig. 23 Polishing finished pen keeper

You may wish to shape the ends of your acrylic. This should be done *before* you heat and bend it.

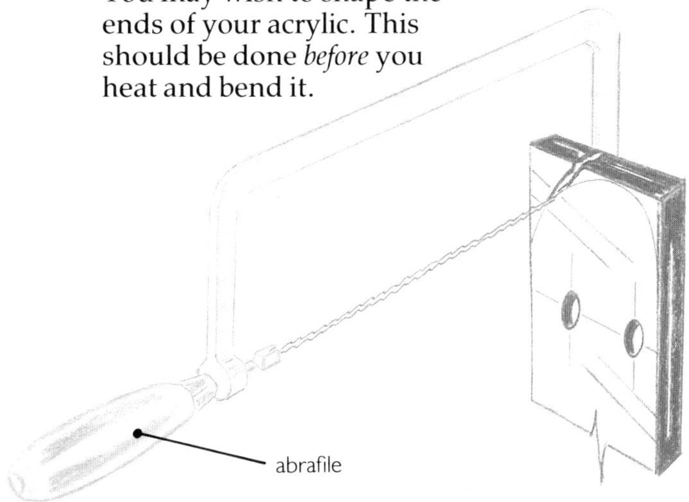

abrafile

Fig. 21 Shaping ends

acrylic to be shaped

wood former

Fig. 22 Heating and bending acrylic

Think about the *order* in which you make any bends.

Things You Will Try

- Draw a flow diagram of the making stages of the pen keeper — see 'Graphics' section for help, page 22.
- Now that you have used acrylic as a material, design a simple letter container or toothbrush holder.

Maze game

Introduction

Fig. 1 A maze 'doodle' on a clay tablet — Cretan civilisation circa 1200 B.C. Thought to be the craftsperson's secret mark

Mazes are found in various shapes and sizes. Trying to solve them is a fascinating and somtimes frustrating task!

A maze is a problem to be solved. The important question is how do we get from the beginning to the end? There are usually false trails to make our task more difficult.

In this project you will design a maze that the player can look down on and see the whole of it and try to work out how to complete the course before starting it.

However, many other mazes are made very big so that they are solved by trial and error. They often have high walls and you can't see the end from the start.

Investigate maze designs for yourself — see *Resources* section, page 18, for how to begin your search.

Did you know?

The **labyrinth** (another word for maze) is one of the most ancient and mysterious symbols known to us. It has been discovered in a number of civilisations, and it is still found to be compulsive and attractive today. (You might have visited a maze, like the one at Hampton Court.)

Hampton Court

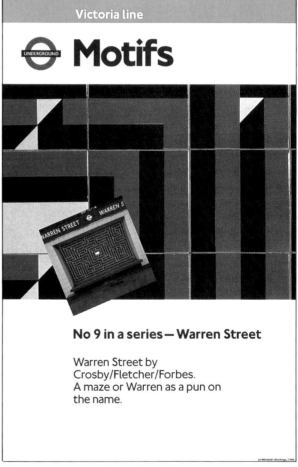

The maze motif on the walls of Warren Street underground station

Julian's Bower, a 13th century turf maze at Alkborough, north Lincolnshire

The brief

To design and make a small hand-held maze game using a ball bearing.

Limitations

- The area for the maze will be 150 mm × 100 mm.
- The walls must be made from straight lengths (no curves!).
- A framework will make the side walls for the maze.
- A clear acrylic top will contain the ball bearing.

Considerations

- A player will hold the game and tilt it to make the ball bearing follow a route.
- Your route should be interesting and enjoyable, to make any player want to try again!
- False trails or detours can make it more difficult to solve.

Look at the *Design process* section, pages 6–7, for ways of beginning to solve problems.

The example shown here is made from wood, but you may choose to use other materials.

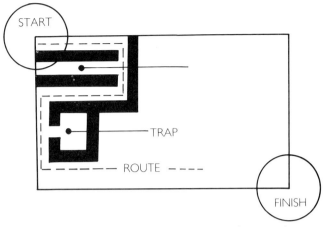

Fig. 2 This partly drawn maze shows you how to plan

PARTS LIST					
ITEM	PART NO.	NO. OFF	L	W	T
MAZE BASE	A	1	150	100	4
LONG SIDE	B	2	176	25	12
SHORT SIDE	C	2	112	25	12
ACRYLIC TOP	D	1	174	124	3
SUPPORTS	F	2	174	5	5
WALLS	/	/	/	5	5
EXTRAS GLUE	AS REQUIRED				
PINS	AS REQUIRED				
JAPANNED SCREWS		4	18x	NO.	6

Fig. 3 Parts list

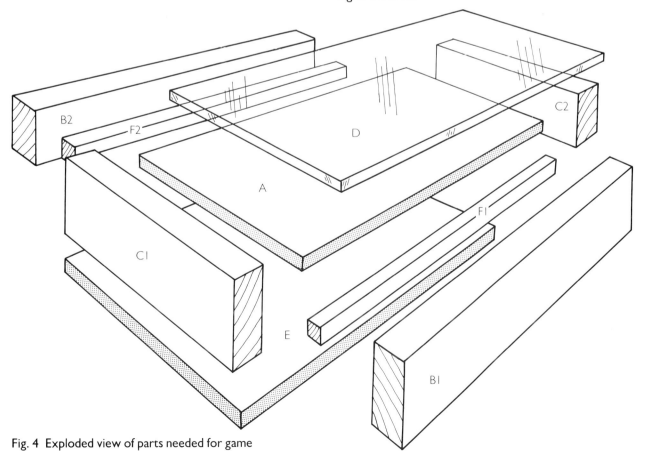

Fig. 4 Exploded view of parts needed for game

Design development

This **procedure** will help you to achieve a successful design.

- Mark out the outline of the base of your maze on a piece of 5 mm squared grid paper to a size of 150 mm × 100 mm.

- Sketch *freehand* the proposed route for the ball bearing.
- Try to make the route long and interesting to follow.
- You should complete *two initial designs* and then choose your best design to develop further.
- You may need to *re-draw* your final design to include any modifications before you are satisfied with the design.

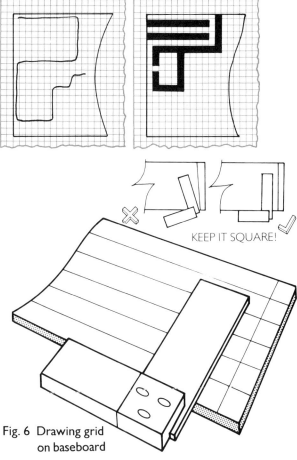

Fig. 5 Designing a maze on squared paper and final neat design

KEEP IT SQUARE!

Fig. 6 Drawing grid on baseboard

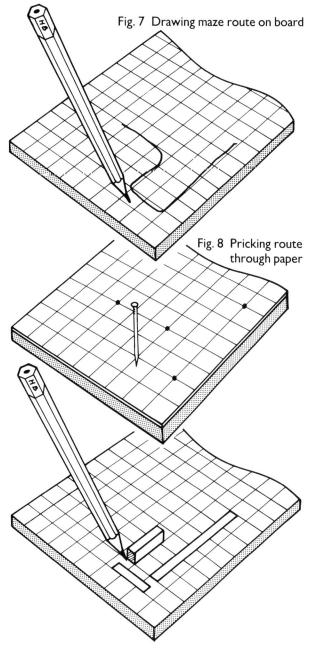

Fig. 7 Drawing maze route on board

Fig. 8 Pricking route through paper

Fig. 9 Drawing in the bases of walls

Transferring the design to the baseboard

- A 10 mm grid may be squared across the board — Fig. 6.
- The route can then be drawn in freehand, allowing for the 5 mm thickness of the walls — Fig. 7.
- An alternative is to lay the paper design over the board and mark through points with a panel pin — Fig. 8.
- Whichever way is chosen, the position of the walls can be traced by using a short length of 'wall' — Fig. 9.

Checklist

- Does your design fit onto the board successfully?
- Have you made any changes during this stage?
- Does your design make a good maze?
- Have you made it a difficult maze to solve?
- Can the ball bearing pass through all of the maze? (This is very important.)

Making your maze

Preparing the wall lengths

With so many small pieces this is a good method to use:

- Measure and cut only a few pieces at a time.
- Smooth all the surfaces, including the ends, with glasspaper.
- Apply a thin layer of glue with a brush to the base of each length.
- Slide each length to and fro slightly to spread the glue.
- Remove any surplus glue with a damp cloth.

Remember to check the gap for the ball bearing

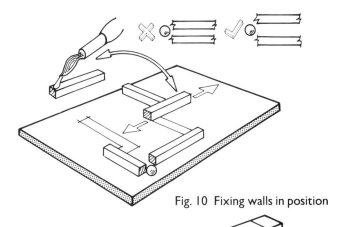

Fig. 10 Fixing walls in position

Making the frame

The lap joint is probably the best way to make the corners

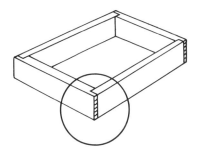

Fig. 11 Frame

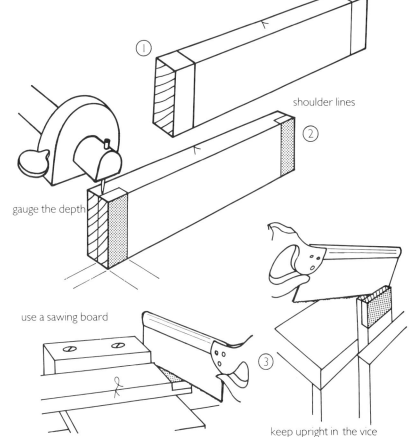

shoulder lines

gauge the depth

use a sawing board

keep upright in the vice

Stages

1 Prepare your wood to size and then mark shoulder lines, using a try square and pencil (only on the two long pieces).

2 Gauge lines half the thickness of the wood and shade in the parts to be cut out.

3 Use a tenon saw to cut the waste.

4 If necessary chisel or file the corner of the joint.

Alternative suggestions for joining the corners are shown on the next page.

tidy the corners

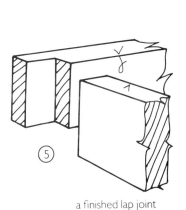

a finished lap joint

Fig. 12 Stages in making a lap joint

51

Assembling the game

Check that all your pieces are smooth and that they fit together squarely. When you assemble the frame, put the pins in at an angle. This is called **dovetail pinning** (Fig. 13).

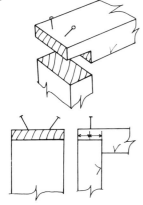

Fig. 13 Dovetail pinning

A pin pusher or a piece of card to protect the surface while holding the pin

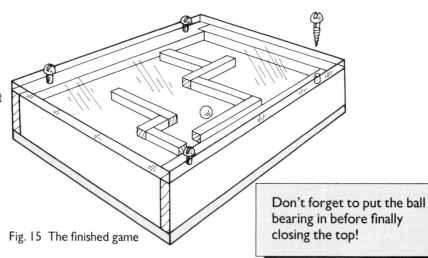

Fig. 14 Assembling the game

Stage 1
Putting together is easier with all the parts upside down. Glue and pin the frame together (or use a frame clamp). Then fix the bottom piece.

Stage 2
Turn the design up the right way and apply your finish. See page 121 for help with finishes.

Fix on the acrylic top. You may use round-head japanned screws or countersunk screws set below the surface.

Fig. 15 The finished game

Don't forget to put the ball bearing in before finally closing the top!

For more help, see *Beginning to make* section, page 117.

Alternative solutions for the frame

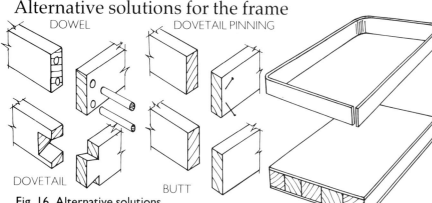

DOWEL   DOVETAIL PINNING

DOVETAIL   BUTT

Fig. 16 Alternative solutions

For more help, see *Assembling the material: wood* on page 116.

All of these alternative solutions have advantages and disadvantages over each other. Can you think what they are?

Look at *Beginning to make*, page 116.

The frame could be made from one length of material that has been formed to shape, e.g. mild steel or plastic. A former may need to be made — see Fig. 14.

Discussion

Here are some simple ways of **evaluating** your design:

● *Playing the maze game*
Have you succeeded in making an interesting maze? Try it out with your friends or a younger brother or sister. What do they think of it?

● *Appearance of the game*
Have you made it look attractive and appealing? Does it give a good combination of colours, or have you used the colour to confuse the player?

● *Construction*
Is it well made and finished? Are the barriers neatly cut and fixed? Can the ball bearing move easily through the maze? Are the joints for the frame a good fit? Is the acrylic top well finished and a tight fit?

These and many other factors will help to make an appealing maze game. Can you think of any more? Write out a list of points showing the merits of your game.

Pupils trying out their maze games

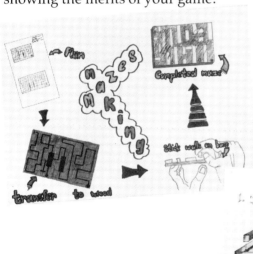

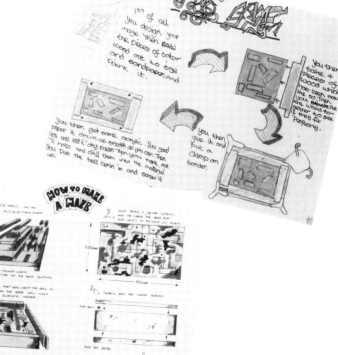

Fig. 17 Nicholas, David and Yolanta did these design sheets to show you how they made their mazes

 Also see the *Graphics for design* section for help with drawing, page 22.

● Now that you have had experience of making a simple maze, use a similar size base to make a new puzzle design. This need not be a maze.

Things You Will Try

● Make a list of all the things that would appeal to you in a commercially-made maze puzzle.
● Describe in four stages how you designed and made your maze — see Fig. 15.

Wind-driven vehicle

The brief

A land yacht

To design and make a small vehicle that can be propelled over land by using wind energy.

Alternative brief

Form a design team to plan and make a scale size model, for example 1:20.

Your design team should have two or three members. Each member should have a clear part to play in the designing.

Think about these points

- How to use wind energy.
- How to direct the wind energy and stay on course.
- The type, size and style of the wheels.
- The number of wheels.
- The position of the wheels and the shape and structure of the vehicle.
- The overall weight and balance.

Can you think of any more?

A different type of land yacht

The sail is a very ancient method of propulsion. But we are still discovering new ways of using it!

Hang glider with skis

Wind surfers

Close up of wind surfer sail

Developing the design

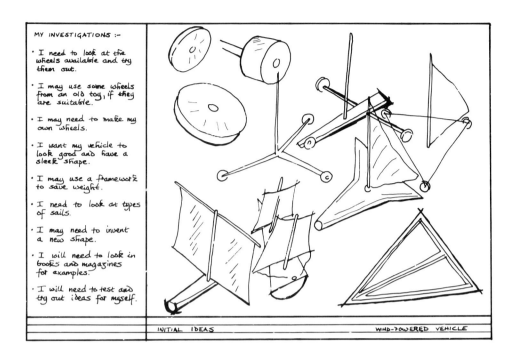

MY INVESTIGATIONS :-

- I need to look at the wheels available and try them out.
- I may use some wheels from an old toy, if they are suitable.
- I may need to make my own wheels.
- I want my vehicle to look good and have a sleek shape.
- I may use a framework to save weight.
- I need to look at types of sails.
- I may need to invent a new shape.
- I will need to look in books and magazines for examples.
- I will need to test and try out ideas for myself.

INITIAL IDEAS   WIND-POWERED VEHICLE

Fig. 1 Initial ideas

What will you choose? Make a list of the features that you think are important.

You will need to **investigate**, that is, to find out things for yourself. Two ways to do this are:

- look at other solutions — see *Resources*, page 18.
- make up test pieces and try them out.

You will need to break down the problem into small parts — this is called **analysis**. Also, you should make a list of important points to think about — these are **considerations**.

Which wheel to use?

The type, size and style of the wheels will be important because:

- Large wheels cover a longer distance every time they do one complete turn or **revolution**.
- Small wheels will have less weight.
- Wide wheels will give a good grip.
- Tyred wheels will ride over bumps more smoothly.
- Smooth wheels will travel faster.

 Look at *Design process*, pages 6–7, for help.

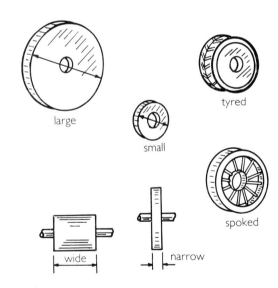

Fig. 2 Some examples of wheels

large *tyred* *small* *spoked* *wide* *narrow*

Things You Will Try

- Fix your chosen wheels to a trial axle to see how they perform.
- Make up a test model from simple materials, for example, straws. Use Plasticine for weight.

Body shape

You can find the best body shape for your design by thinking about either:

Function — this is simply the job that the body has to do, e.g. hold the wheels, sail, etc.

OR:

Style/aesthetics — you may decide upon a particular appearance or a streamlined shape.

A good design should have the best of both function and style/aesthetics.

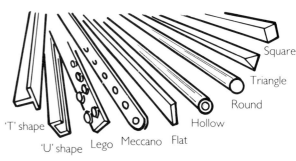

Fig. 3 Types of construction pieces

'T' shape   'U' shape   Lego   Meccano   Flat   Hollow   Round   Triangle   Square

The wheel layout

The wheels will need to be fixed to an axle and to the framework of your vehicle. How many wheels will you use? Two, three, four or more?

Think about these points

● Two wheels could be unstable — how would you solve this?
● Three wheels give more stability but where will you place them?
● Four wheels have the most stability but what other problems do they cause?

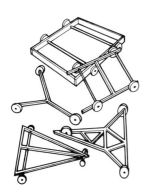

Fig. 4 Frameworks with wheels

Streamlining (aerofoil shape)

Streamlining any shape that moves will help it to move faster and more easily.

Investigate

Aeroplane designs and the sleek shape of modern yachts or cars.

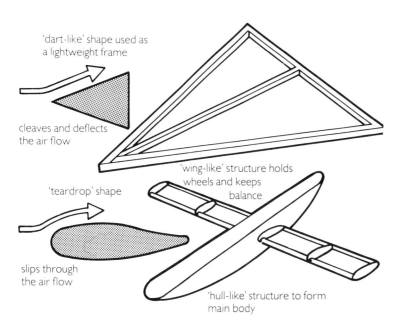

'dart-like' shape used as a lightweight frame

cleaves and deflects the air flow

'teardrop' shape

slips through the air flow

'wing-like' structure holds wheels and keeps balance

'hull-like' structure to form main body

Fig. 5 Design a vehicle body

stability

Fig. 7 Stability of 2, 3 and 4 wheels

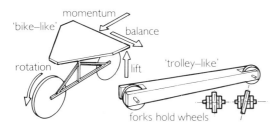

momentum

'bike–like'   balance

rotation   lift   'trolley–like'

forks hold wheels

Fig. 6 'Bike like' and 'trolley like' shapes

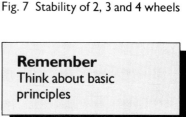

Remember
Think about basic principles

Types of sail

Catching the wind energy

The traditional wind-catching device is the sail. People have used it over the centuries as a free source of power.

In the environment the use of wind energy has the advantage of being quiet, non-polluting and renewable.

The two popular types of sail are the **square rigging** and the **triangular yacht sail.** The list gives some of their advantages and disadvantages. Can you think of any more?

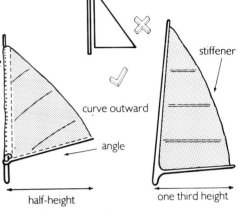

Fig. 9 Triangular sail

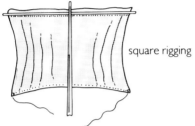

Fig. 8 Square rigged sail

Square-rigged sail
● Easy to construct.
● Usually placed in the centre of the mast.
● A large area to catch a good volume of wind.
● Can be difficult to control the 'rig'.
● Performs best when the wind is fully behind the sail.
● Difficult to move when the wind direction changes.

Triangular yacht sail
● A simple shape but it needs to be constructed carefully.
● Mast is placed on one side of the sail.
● Sail area usually less than square-rigging.
● It is easy to control.
● You can move the sail as the wind direction changes.
● You can control the wind energy quite well.

Faster than the wind?

The modern racing yacht uses the huge 'spinnaker' sail set at the front of the boat to get extra speed. This makes the boat move much faster, but when the wind dies, the spinnaker deflates and it will drag and slow the boat.

Think about these points
● The type of sail or an alternative, e.g. a wing-like structure.
● The material for the sail.
● The material for the mast, stiff or flexible?
● How to fix the sail to the mast.
● The 'rigging' needed.

Yacht with spinnaker sail

57

Making it work

Attention to detail

You will have many small parts to make if your wind-powered vehicle is to perform well. Some ideas are given here, but you will need to think of others for yourself.

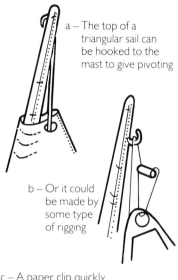

a – The top of a triangular sail can be hooked to the mast to give pivoting

b – Or it could be made by some type of rigging

c – A paper clip quickly makes a hook

Fig. 10 Making the sail movable

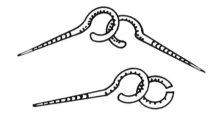

Fig. 11 Using two eyelets to make a universal link

Fig. 12 Horse-shoe swivel

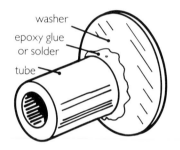

washer
epoxy glue or solder
tube

Fig. 14 Bearing on end of axle

Fig. 15 Use and reshape standard bolts

mast can be removed

Fig. 13 Main mast in a hole

Fig. 16a Panel pins can make pivots

Fig. 16c Stiff wire can be bent into a loop

Fig. 16b Plastic tubing makes a flexible connection

Finding out more

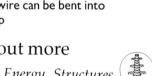

Look at the *Energy, Structures* and *Mechanisms* sections for help in **applying** an idea — pages 76–93.

Look at the *Beginning to make* section for help in **realising** an idea — page 198.

Think about these points

- Your good ideas can solve a difficult problem.
- Try to test an idea and perhaps make changes — these are **modifications**.
- Take care to be accurate.
- Remember that care with details will create a better performance in the end.

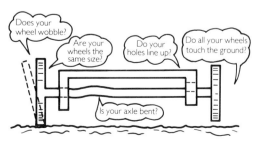

Does your wheel wobble?
Are your wheels the same size?
Do your holes line up?
Do all your wheels touch the ground?
Is your axle bent?

Fig. 17 Some problems that you might have!

Trying it out

Time to test

However carefully you design, it is only by testing the practical model that you really find out if your design works.

Indoors you can make use of equipment to **simulate** the wind, for example a hairdryer or vacuum cleaner. It is only outdoors that you will be able to achieve true performance. Remember that the wind is very unpredictable. For a fair trial you will need a sheltered area, such as a playground.

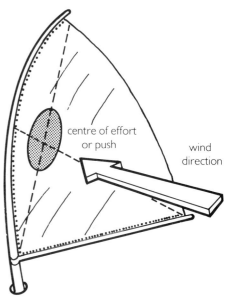

Fig. 18 Wind hitting a triangular sail

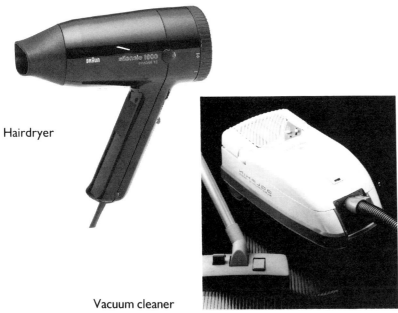

Hairdryer

Vacuum cleaner

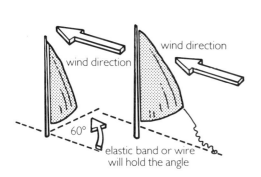

Fig. 19 Keeping sail at best angle

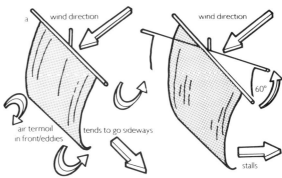

Fig. 20 Wind hitting a square sail

RUN NO.	DISTANCE (m)	TIME (s)	DIS/TIME	AVERAGE
1				
2				
3				

Fig. 21 Test chart for a vehicle

To check the performance you can devise a simple test chart, like Fig. 21.

Think about these points

- A successful practical model will need many ingredients.
- You have to consider and solve many design and practical problems.
- Testing will show if you have been successful or not.
- Look out for inefficient parts in your design, e.g. the wheels.
- Can you learn from the ideas of others?
- You may still need to alter and modify your design after you have tested it.

The fun board

Understanding mechanisms is not easy. You can make it easier to learn about them if you make a project that uses some simple mechanisms. Taking a fun approach can make it interesting to do, and amusing for others to use.

A 'fun board' is a flat board that demonstrates the use of a mechanism in a humorous or interesting way by basing it on a theme, such as a popular event, a sport or a nursery rhyme.

> **Look around at things that use mechanisms.**

The brief

To design and make a fun board, e.g. for a young child, that uses one or more of the following mechanisms:

● pulleys
● cams
● gears
● levers and linkages
● crank and slider
● ratchet and pawl.

Here are some examples of odd or amusing things that use mechanisms.

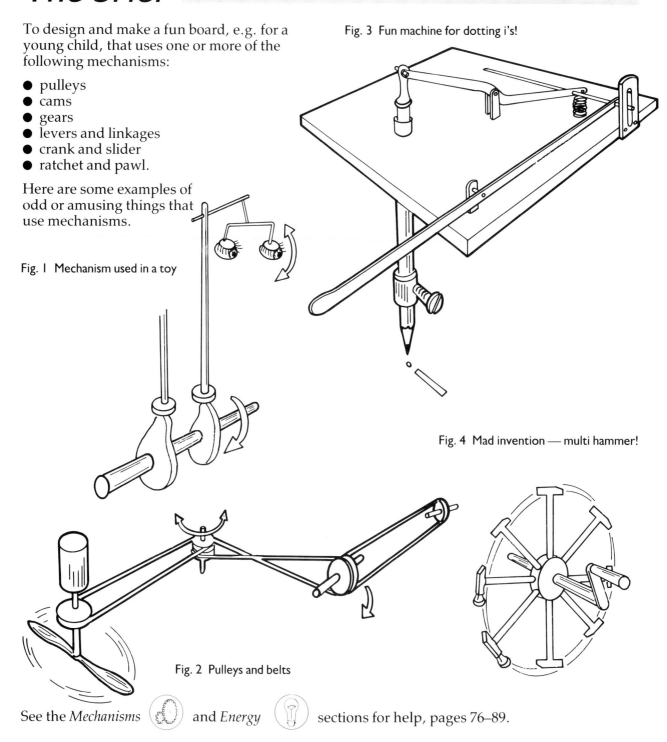

Fig. 1 Mechanism used in a toy

Fig. 3 Fun machine for dotting i's!

Fig. 4 Mad invention — multi hammer!

Fig. 2 Pulleys and belts

See the *Mechanisms* and *Energy* sections for help, pages 76–89.

Fun use of crank and slider

These examples show how *rotary* motion can be converted to *linear* (straight line) motion.

See pages 80–89 for more help with the theory of mechanisms.

Fig. 5 'Punch-up-in-the-park' machine

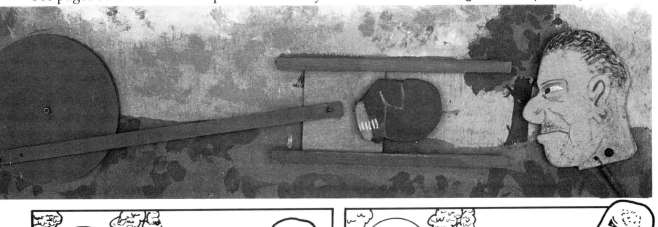

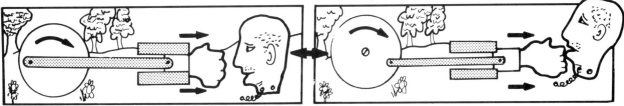

Fig. 6 Little Miss Muffet
fun board

Modelling

Use a model to try out your ideas and get the *correct scale*. You will find help with modelling on page 14.

Example: modelling a crank and slider in card

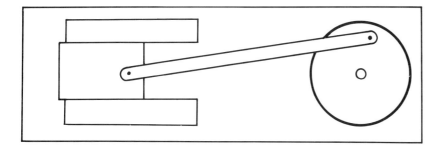

Fig. 7 Crank and slider

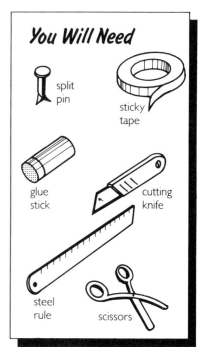

You Will Need

split pin

sticky tape

glue stick

cutting knife

steel rule

scissors

Fig. 8

Mark out pieces on card.

Fig. 9

Build up overhang in layers.

Fig. 11

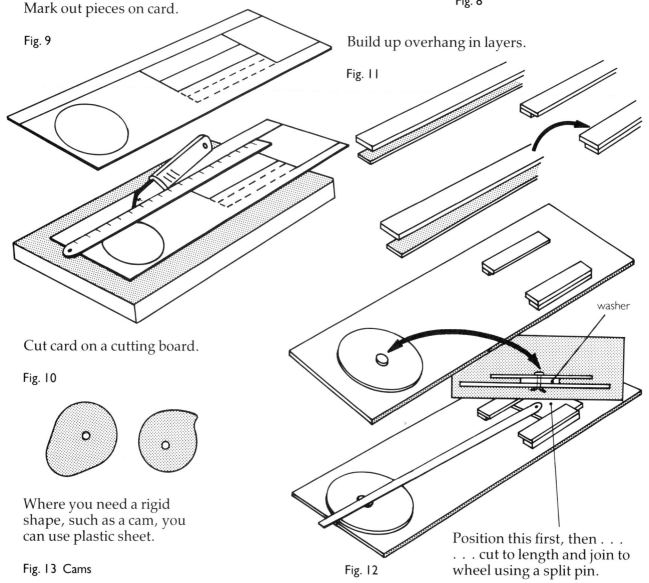

Cut card on a cutting board.

Fig. 10

Where you need a rigid shape, such as a cam, you can use plastic sheet.

Fig. 13 Cams

Fig. 12

washer

Position this first, then . . .
. . . cut to length and join to wheel using a split pin.

Hints for making

Here are some simple ways of making the mechanisms for your fun board.

Making a pulley

The middle disc should have a smaller diameter than the outer ones.

A screw or nut and bolt will secure your pulley to the baseboard.

Use a hole saw cutter to cut out the wooden discs.

To keep a sliding part in place, two pieces of material of different widths can be stuck together.

Fig. 14 Making wooden pulleys

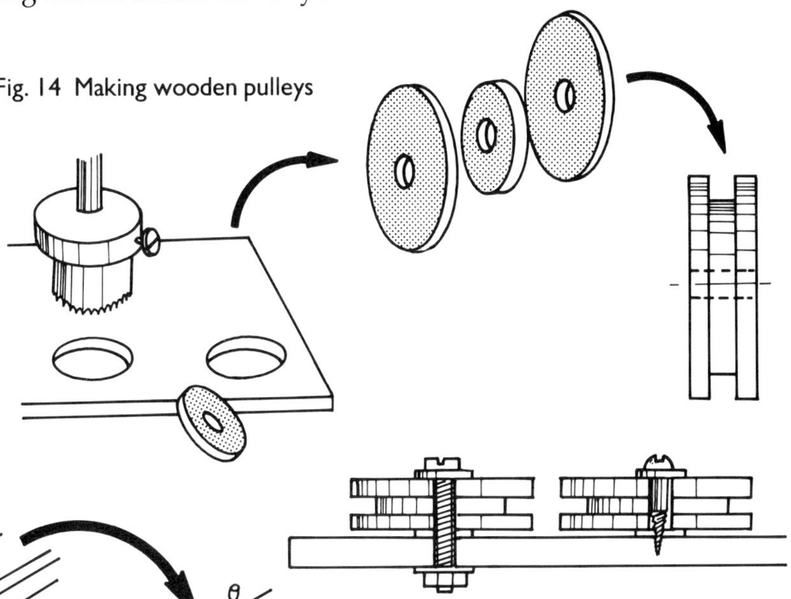

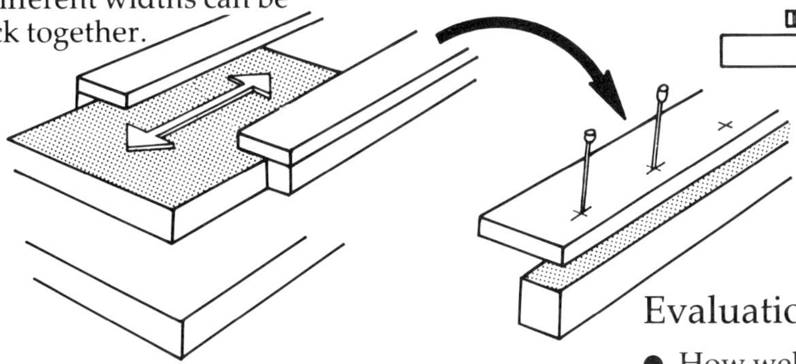

Fig. 15 Making runner for slider (wood)

Making a gear

A simple gear can be made by gluing round pegs into a circular disc.

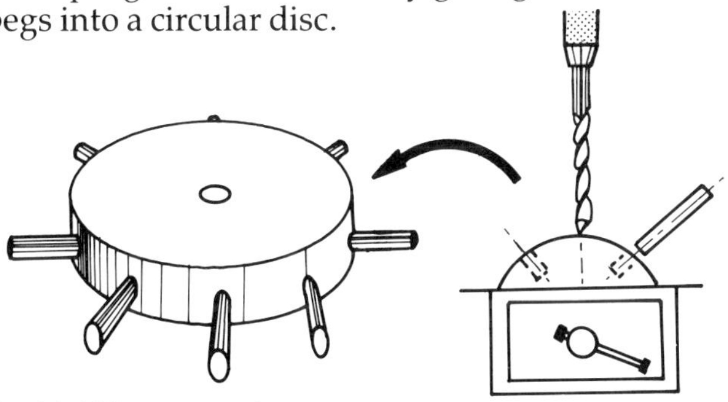

Fig. 16 Making a wooden gear

Making a cam

Cut the shape that you want out of paper and stick it onto your material. Drill the centre hole before you remove the paper.

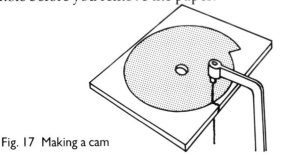

Fig. 17 Making a cam

Evaluation

● How well does your mechanism operate?
● Does it attract attention and provide amusement over and over again?

Things You Will Try

● Make sketches of four things around you that use mechanisms.
● Make simple working models, using card, of the mechanisms that you have investigated.
● Plan an amusing way of demonstrating the use of simple mechanisms to do an impractical job, that is, something that hasn't got a real use. Investigate 'Heath Robinson' designs (in a library). See also *Mechanisms*, pages 80–89.

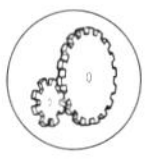

● You can add simple electronics — see *Electronics*, page 68 — to create more interest, make parts move, or make a noise.

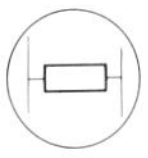

● You could also 'interface' your project to a computer — see *Computers*, page 72 — to be able to control it.

Light-barrier puzzle

The brief

To design and make a puzzle that uses an electronic sensor. The player has to control the path of a beam of light to be able to solve a 'code' within a few moves, and so activate a light sensor.

Fig. 1

Background

The need to communicate messages by using some type of technology happens regularly in our modern society. For example many telephone messages are now sent using light waves that travel along optical cables known as fibre optics.

Here you are given the beginning of a project where light waves can be used to provide an amusing (or frustrating) puzzle similar to the sending of a complex message.

You are expected to use the knowledge you have gained in designing and making to work out your own full solution, given the starting points suggested here.

The mechanism will be hidden from the player.

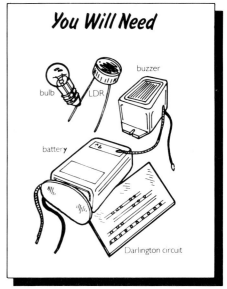

You Will Need

Fig. 2

Consider

A number of barriers prevent a message being sent by the light source. In the barrier is a hole that allows the light through. Each barrier has the hole in a different position. To succeed, the player has to line up the holes in the correct order (this is called a 'code').

Here are two examples to show how you could develop the game.

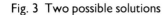

Fig. 3 Two possible solutions

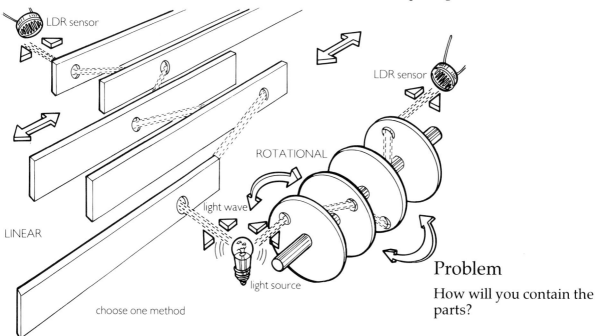

Problem

How will you contain the parts?

Developing the design

Some suggestions

Look at the *Electronics* section for help with a circuit — page 68.

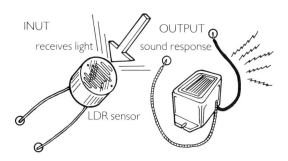

Fig. 4 Input/output

Think
- How can you give the player clues to finding the solution?
- How will a single move by a barrier be made and checked? For example, a peg in a hole.
- How will you make all the holes line up?
- How will the holes in the circles line up?

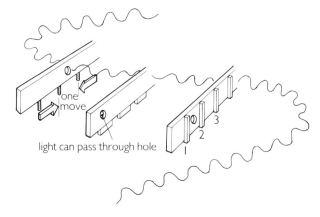

Fig. 5 Slide in barriers with holes

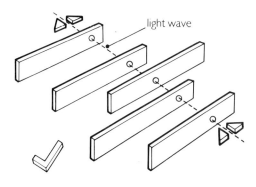

Fig. 6 All holes lined up

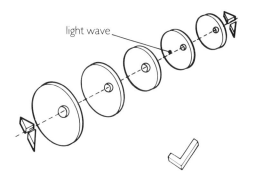

Fig. 7 Circular barriers with holes

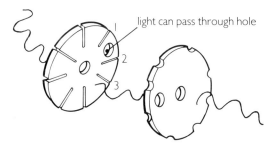

Fig. 8 Two possible circular barriers

Checklist
- Does your circuit work?
- Can all the holes line up?
- What counts as a move?
- Can you count each move?
- Is the mechanism completely hidden from the player?
- How can you prevent cheating?

Slotted structure

The brief

To design and make a slotted structure, which might be a
building toy for a child or a sculpture.

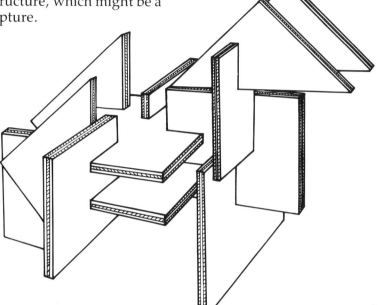

Fig. 1 Slotted structure

Limitations

- Your structure must use the equivalent of
  ten squares of material.
- You may cut no more than four squares in
  half diagonally — see Fig. 2.
- Each plywood square is 60 × 60 × 4mm.
- The slots cut in each piece must be at right
  angles to an edge — see Fig. 3.

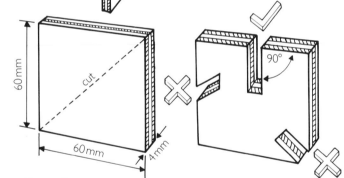

Fig. 2 Cutting squares in half   Fig. 3 Cutting slots

Considerations

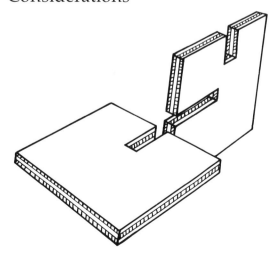

Fig. 4 Slotting pieces together

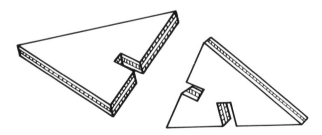

Think about

- How individual pieces could be slotted —
  see Fig. 4.
- Will your slotted structure have a practical
  use, for example, to hold something?
- How can you make your slotted structure
  stable?

Designing and making your structure

Designing

- It will be easier to model your ideas than to try to draw them.
- An ideal material with which to model this design is card.
- The more models you make, the better your final design will be.
- Use scissors to cut the slots in the card.
- Remember, you may cut no more than four squares diagonally.
- Continue to build your structure until you have used all the pieces of card.
- Repeat this until you have a structure that you like.
- Number carefully each piece of your chosen structure.

Making

- Before marking out and cutting the slots you will need to:

  1 Mark out and cut diagonal pieces (if you have used them).
  2 Number each piece as in your model.
  3 Glasspaper the edges of each piece.

- Mark out all the slots. Use your try square to make sure that your lines are at 90 degrees to each edge, see Fig. 6. Shade in the parts to be cut out.
- Use a dovetail saw to cut the depth on both sides of the slot. Cut on the waste side otherwise the slot may be too loose, see Fig. 7. Cut the waste piece out with a coping saw, see Fig. 8.
- Use the flat file to smooth the bottom of the slot, Fig. 9.

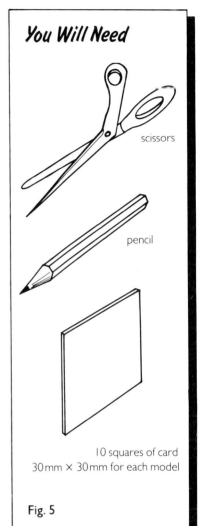

You Will Need

scissors

pencil

I0 squares of card 30mm × 30mm for each model

Fig. 5

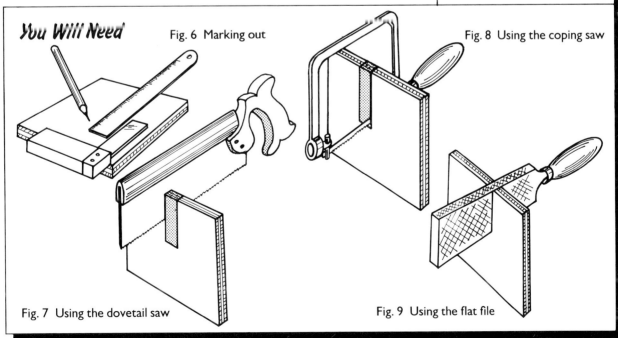

You Will Need

Fig. 6 Marking out

Fig. 8 Using the coping saw

Fig. 7 Using the dovetail saw

Fig. 9 Using the flat file

Look at the *Structures* section, page 90, for an understanding of the wide use of structures in nature, and some of the things we have made in the world.

Electronics

Electricity and electronics

About electricity

Electricity is a phenomenon. You can't see it, smell it, or hear it — but you can see its effects as energy.

For example, when you turn on a light by pressing a switch, or control the volume on a radio, you are using electricity. We think of the electrical energy as flowing round a **circuit**. A circuit might be just a loop of wire, or it might be several electrical components joined together by wires or a **conductive track** — Fig. 2. The electricity you are using is the movement of a small part of the atom — called an electron — along the electrical wires.

Fig. 1 Input and output

Machines that use electronics

In our experiments and models the e.m.f. is supplied by a **battery** or from the mains supply through a power pack. A battery is marked with the e.m.f. it provides, e.g. 9 V. It has a positive (+) and a negative (−) terminal. On circuit diagrams — see Fig. 3 — the current flows from the positive terminal through the circuit to the negative terminal. This is called 'conventional' current because it was labelled this way in the early discoveries about electricity. We now believe the electrons flow from the negative side to the positive! But the earlier 'convention' is still used in diagrams.

The flow of electricity is called an electric **current**. It is measured in amperes or **amps** (A). But this is a large unit for most small electrical circuits, where the small currents used are measured in milliamps (mA) or microamperes (μA).

The electricity can only flow if it is driven round the circuit by a force. We call this force the **electromotive force** (e.m.f.). It is measured in **volts** (V); a small e.m.f. may be measured in millivolts (mV). You may find it useful to compare the flow of electric current to water in the pipes of a plumbing system. But this is only a simple comparison — i.e. why don't electrons squirt out of the end of a wire, as water does from a pipe?

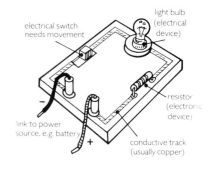

Fig. 2 Simple circuit

About electronics

Electronics is about using simple electronic devices, such as transistors, put together in circuits to make things work. The electronic circuits can be used in complex machines such as computers, radios or washing machines.

Most electronic devices are different from common electrical devices such as switches. They appear not to have any working parts. They seem to carry out their task mysteriously! But to work, as in any circuit, they must be joined together to make a continuous electronic circuit.

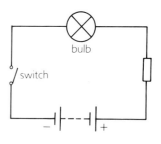

Fig. 3 Circuit diagram

electronic system

'your design work, using electronics could make an ¯ifference, e.g. something could be made to move, ¬ake a sound.

..ctronic system can be divided into three basic parts: 1 — input, 2 — process, 3 — output. The 'input' is similar to our senses of sight, hearing, touch, smell and taste — it tells the 'system' what is happening. The 'process' is a little like our brain — it reacts to the input and sometimes makes decisions. It is the heart of the system. The 'output' is what the system does.

This is an example:
INPUT — light sensor
PROCESS — electronic circuit reacts to change of light
OUTPUT — buzzer alarm sounds

This could be used for a simple burglar alarm.

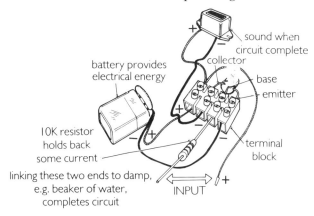

Fig. 6 Prototype — simple damp detector circuit

A practical circuit

It is difficult to do anything with just one transistor. But here is a circuit that will light a bulb or sound a buzzer when the circuit is *completed*, by putting the two ends of wire in water (or held together with damp fingers).

This very simple circuit uses a 'terminal block', (a connector made from plastic), to join up the connections. This means that it can be made quickly and tested, with no need to solder any components.

Which leg of the transistor is which?

It is often difficult to recognise the correct leg or connection of a transistor. However, remember that the emitter is the nearest to the tag. Then read clockwise for the base and collector when seen from below (see Fig. 5).

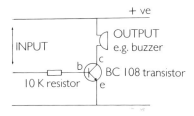

Fig. 7 Circuit diagram for simple damp detector

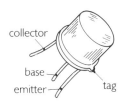

Fig. 4 A transistor is usually a tin can with three legs sticking out

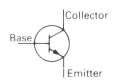

Fig. 5 Circuit symbol for NPN type transistor

What can I do with a transistor?

A **transistor** is an electronic device that can control the flow of electric current rather like a tap for the flow of water in a water pipe. It can instantly switch the current on and off like a light switch; or gradually like a dimmer control. Sometimes a transistor is called a 'solid state switch'.

So a transistor can be used to control the flow, as well as to increase the flow of electricity to another component. This makes it a useful device in many different circuits.

Think about
- What is electric current, and what units do we use to measure it?
- What is the electromotive force (e.m.f.), and what units do we use to measure it?
- What do we use to supply the e.m.f.?

Darlington pair

The transistor in the simple circuit of Figs 6 and 7 works as a switch. When the water completes the circuit, a small electric current flows through the base of the transistor. This makes the transistor switch on the current through the buzzer.

But with only one transistor, quite a large current must flow to the base before the switch works. If you put a small electric motor in place of the buzzer, it may not work well. However, if you use two transistors combined together — called a **Darlington pair** — the circuit of Fig. 6 can be made much more sensitive, and able to control larger currents — Fig. 8. A very small current flowing to the base of the first transistor will switch on a much bigger current through the motor — big enough to make the motor work. Try this as an experiment.

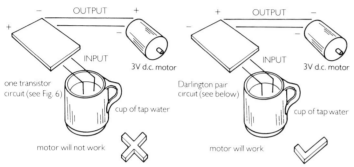

Fig. 8 Experiment with damp detector circuits

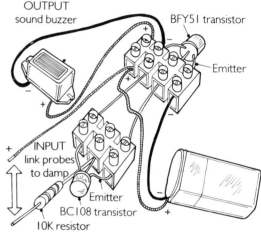

Fig. 9 Prototype Darlington pair circuit (terminal block)

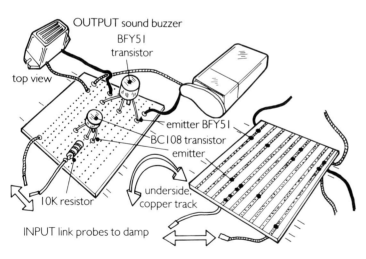

Fig. 10 Prototype Darlington pair circuit (Veroboard)

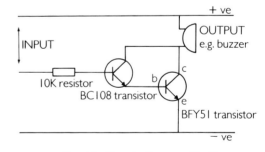

Fig. 11 Circuit diagram (Darlington pair)

It is important to remember that although transistors might appear 'magic', they cannot increase the overall current or voltages in a circuit; they only control what is available.

The Darlington pair circuit can provide a building block for many projects. See page 64, the *Light-barrier puzzle* project, as an example where this circuit can be used.

Project

Design a suitable casing and probe so that you can use the Darlington pair circuit as a simple damp detector or water level indicator.

Output

The output of a circuit can take many forms:
Power — a d.c. motor
Light — a torch bulb
Sound — a buzzer

Identifying basic components

Basic components are supported by many other electrical devices like coils, relays, special variable resistors, etc. If you need to use these you may need the help of more specialist books.

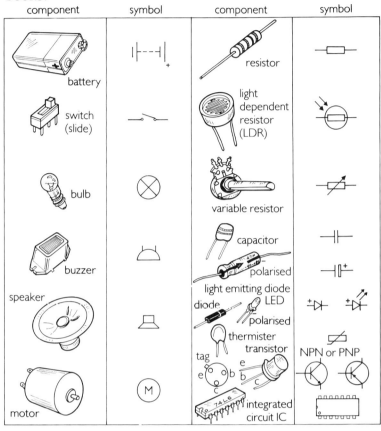

component	symbol	component	symbol

Fig. 12 Table of electronic components

These basic components are the ones that are used most frequently in simple circuits. In some projects you may need to use some additional specialised components or devices.

Key words

A **capacitor** is an electrical component which stores electrical charge or energy. d.c. electric current cannot flow through a capacitor.

A **diode** allows electric current to flow in one direction only.

A **resistor** will restrict the flow of electric current.

A **transistor** is a sort of remote control electrical tap (see page 69), which can vary or stop the flow of electric current.

A **polarised** component can only be connected one way round, i.e. the positive (+) must be connected to the positive part of the circuit, e.g. electrolytic capacitor.

An **integrated circuit** contains more than one component (like a transistor). In one device, there are often many thousands of components.

Circuit — Electricity flows through the circuit which links the components together (electricity cannot flow where there is no circuit).

Components — These are the parts used to make up an electronic system. They may be electronic like a transistor or electrical like a switch.

 # Computers

Computer graphics

Computer graphics are a new electronic way in which you can express design ideas. A high resolution colour monitor and a keyboard are the basic equipment. But extra devices like an electronic pen, a joystick, a mouse or a touch tablet help with graphics.

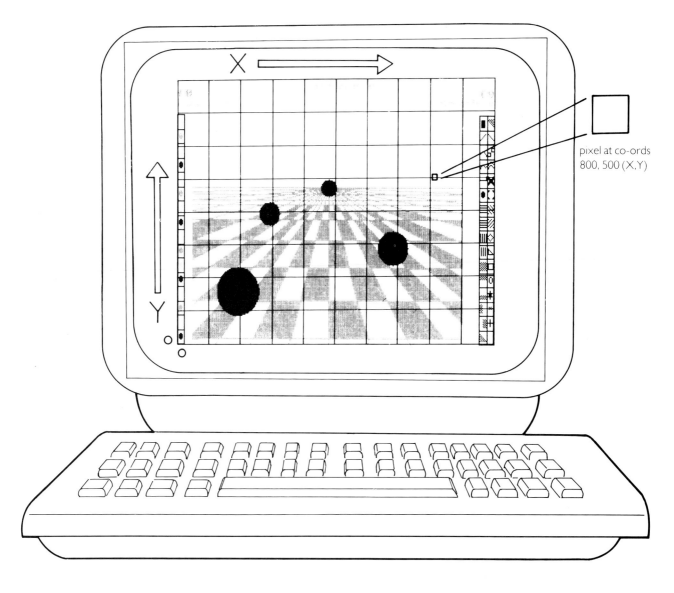

pixel at co-ords
800, 500 (X,Y)

Fig. 1 Computer: keyboard and VDU with graphics display

Key ideas

- The screen is divided into a grid of small squares called pixels — picture cells.
- To describe a position on the screen, cartesian co-ordinates of X and Y are most often used. For example 800,500 would mean a point at 800 units across (X) and 500 units up (Y), see Fig. 1.

- The pixels can be of different intensity — in a range from very bright to dull.
- The pixels can be lit in many different colours.
- To make up a drawing the computer will need to be given the positions, brightness and colour of all the pixels on the screen.

Graphic packages

You do not need to write computer programs yourself. A graphic package can give you a wide range of facilities for design.

Regular shapes like rectangles and circles are easy to draw. Colouring in can be quick and ideas can be compared on the computer screen.

You can record your ideas by using photographs and prints taken from the screen. Examples of these are shown below.

Fig. 2 Design for a wine glass

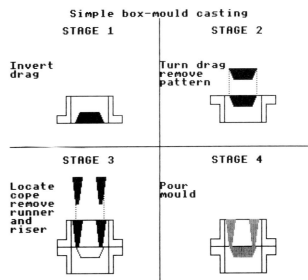

Fig. 4 Box-mould casting process

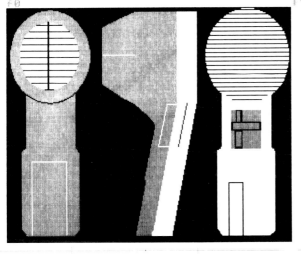

Fig. 3 Planning a kitchen layout

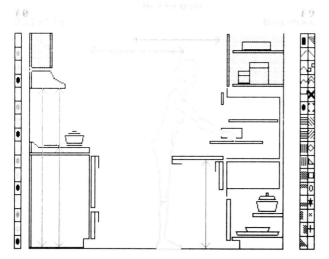

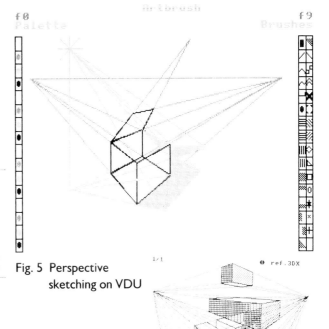

Fig. 5 Perspective sketching on VDU

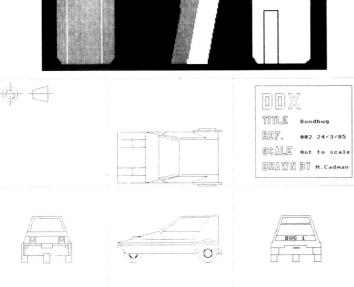

Fig. 6 Orthographic drawing on VDU

Computer control

Computer control is about using a microcomputer to *alter* or *detect* the action of something. The action can be either an input, such as a switch closing; or an output, for example, a motor starting and stopping.

How do I control things?

Using a computer for control is easy — when you know how!

It can seem difficult at first because there are new things to understand. Some of these you will need to learn. But often you can use a kit — like 'LEGO Control' — to let you try out things by experiment.

Which computer should I use?

All microcomputers can be used to control things. You may have seen a computer controlling a printer. This is an example of how a computer sends out **signals** to control the action of a complex device.

The Acorn BBC Micro series of computers are a popular choice for control. You can use a **computer language** (such as BASIC) to control them directly.

However, you will usually use special **software** that can make things simpler to do and to understand.

Machines that use computer control

Using computer control in your project can add excitement and interest.

Key words

Hardware — the equipment used, e.g. computer.
Software — programs which instruct the computer.
Program — a series of instructions in a computer language such as BASIC.
Memory — electronic store of information. The computer usually operates from ROM (Read Only Memory). Programs are in RAM (Random Access Memory).
Address — the place in the memory where a particular piece of information is stored.
Port — a connection to the computer usually as a plug with special lines to the main microchip or central processor unit operating inside a computer. The port will only operate when the correct memory address is used in order to send and receive information.

Control examples

For computer control it is usual to have an **interface board** between the computer and the devices to be controlled.

What is the interface for?

It provides:

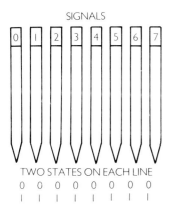

- protection for the computer from possible faults.
- connections to the computer, which may be input or output.
- transistor or relay circuits which can amplify or control higher currents than the computer itself. (See *Electronics* section, page 68.)
- a separate power supply to drive devices.
- often an LED display to show what is happening.

Care and safety

- Never plug things directly to the computer.
- You should always use an interface board when trying out any projects you make.
- Always be sure that electrical connections are properly made. In particular, the ground or negative wires must be connected to the correct terminal.
- Check that any soldering of electronic components is good.

Control lines

The computer controls devices by sending signals in **binary** form, that is as '0's and '1's.

On an eight-bit computer eight lines (usually numbered 0 to 7) can control eight events.

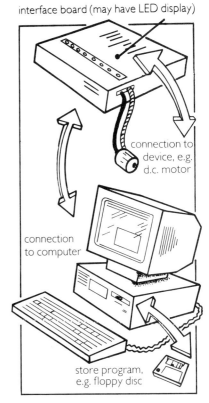

Fig. 7 **Parts of computer control system**

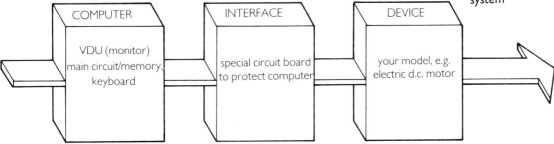

Fig. 8 **Block diagram of basic control system**

SIGNALS

0 1 2 3 4 5 6 7

TWO STATES ON EACH LINE

0 0 0 0 0 0 0 0
1 1 1 1 1 1 1 1

Fig. 9 **Binary signals**

Things You Will Try

- List the parts of a computer control system.
- Make a checklist of places where poor electrical connections may occur.
- Use the equipment and software that you have to drive a d.c. motor, forward and reverse.
- Use your computer graphics package to design:

  — a house and the surrounding landscape
  — some form of transport for the future
  — a cover for a recording by your favourite music artist or group.

 # Energy

About energy

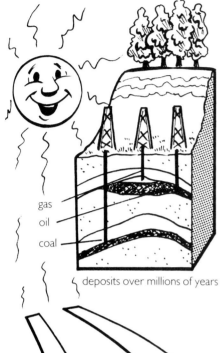

gas
oil
coal

deposits over millions of years

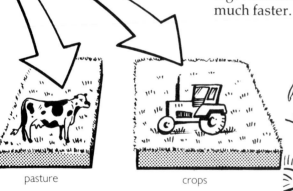

pasture

crops

Fig. 1 Sun's energy — fossil fuels, plants, animals

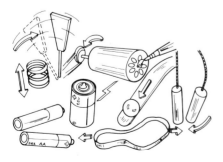

Fig. 3 Energy sources you can use

Energy is power. Designing and making often involves using energy in one form or another, so it is useful for you to understand something about it.

All energy in nature comes from the Sun. On Earth, some of this energy has been stored for millions of years in the **fossil fuels** (coal, gas, oil). It is also evident in the tidal waves of the oceans and the prevailing winds.

When fossil fuels are used they give up the power that nature has stored, once and for all. But sources like tidal waves and wind power can be used over and over again; they are **renewable**.

The Sun provides the heat and light for plants, animals and people to grow and live. Without the energy from the Sun, life on Earth would not be possible at all.

Using energy

We use energy all the time, simply to breathe or to keep our bodies warm. But when we exercise or move around quickly, e.g. when riding a bike or running upstairs, we use up energy much faster.

Fig. 2 We use up energy all the time

There are many different sources of energy. In projects you will probably find these the most useful sources of energy: mechanical, electrical, wind, water and gravity. Some examples are shown in Fig. 3.

Work and energy

To make something happen in your project you will need to use some form of energy. The action that takes place will be the **work** done by the energy source, for example, when a spring is compressed and then returns to its original shape.

Energy needs

In the modern world it is important that we use and manage our energy **resources** very carefully.

There is only a limited supply of fossil fuels. They will eventually run out. As an alternative to fossil fuels, modern technology developed the use of nuclear power to supply many of our energy needs. But there are problems with nuclear power; health risks and hazardous waste that is difficult to dispose of.

New ways of using energy that are 'pollution free', such as wind turbines and tidal wave power, are being developed for the future. These are also renewable — they can be used over and over again.

It is important to remember that energy cannot be created or destroyed, but it can change its form.

Fig. 4 Modern energy sources

Changing energy

It is not always convenient to use natural or produced forms of energy directly. Sometimes they will need to be converted from one form to another, see Fig. 5.

direct use

indirect use

Fig. 5 Direct and indirect use of energy sources

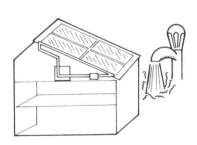

Fig. 6 Solar panel heating water

In mechanisms, each time energy changes from one form to another, some of the energy will be lost. This means that the mechanism will not be 100 per cent efficient.

$$\text{Efficiency (\%)} = \frac{\text{useful work out}}{\text{work input}} \times 100\%$$

Saving energy

In today's world we use a lot of energy. Because of the increased *demand* for energy, our natural sources of energy are in short supply and the cost to the customer has increased. Many people are therefore looking at ways of saving energy.

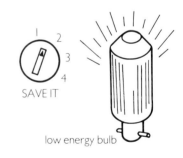

SAVE IT

low energy bulb

Fig. 8 Energy saving

Fig. 7 Car and bike

Which costs the Earth's resources least, bike or car?

Think about the efficiency of any mechanisms you may use in projects. Also look at the *Mechanisms* section, page 80, for practical ideas.

Using energy

Using energy in a project can make it more exciting because
you can actually see something happen.

How can you use energy in your project?

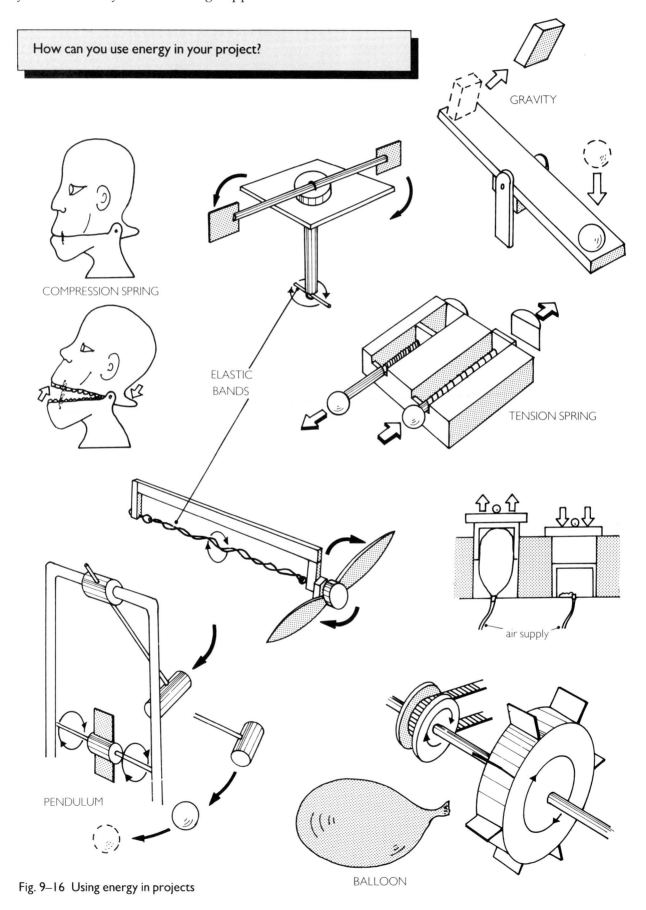

GRAVITY

COMPRESSION SPRING

ELASTIC
BANDS

TENSION SPRING

air supply

PENDULUM

BALLOON

Fig. 9–16 Using energy in projects

The energy source that you use should be the one that is best suited to the problem that you need to solve — as you can see in these examples.

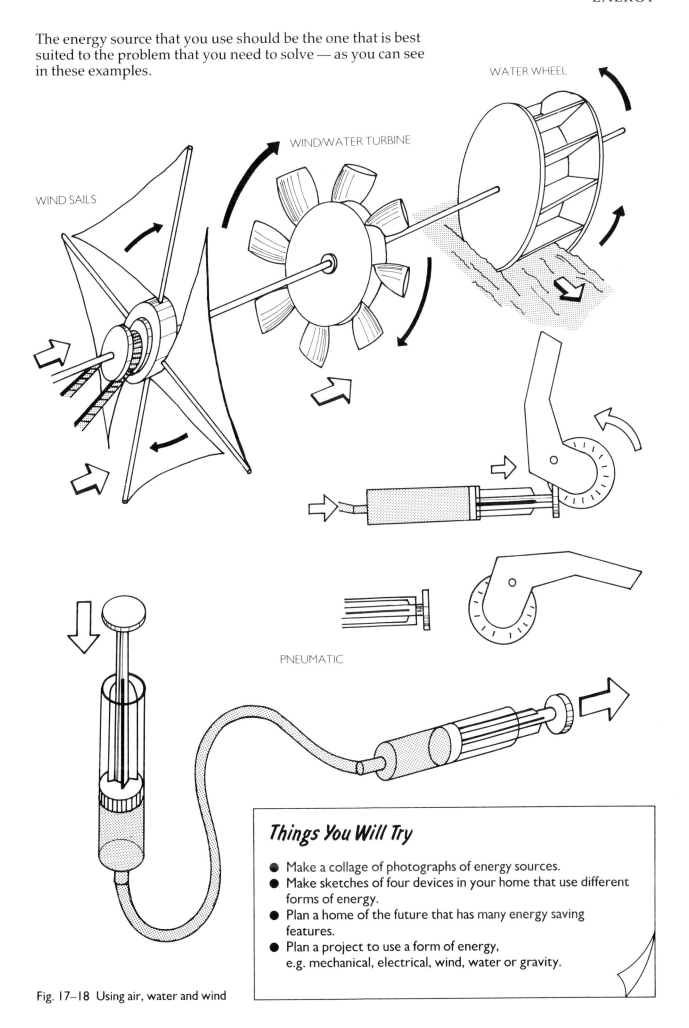

Fig. 17–18 Using air, water and wind

Things You Will Try

- Make a collage of photographs of energy sources.
- Make sketches of four devices in your home that use different forms of energy.
- Plan a home of the future that has many energy saving features.
- Plan a project to use a form of energy, e.g. mechanical, electrical, wind, water or gravity.

Mechanisms

About mechanisms

When you think of a mechanism you might think of a **machine**. This is because mechanisms are what make a machine work. Often the pieces of a machine are called its **mechanical parts**.

So, a machine is a system of parts working together. In a simple machine you can see the mechanical parts clearly — Fig. 1. In a complex machine it is not so clear — Fig. 3.

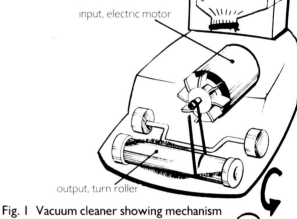

input, electric motor

output, turn roller

Fig. I Vacuum cleaner showing mechanism

Fig. 2 Plant watering spray

press trigger

Input and output

The machines or mechanisms that you use help to make things easier to do. Often machines make our lives more pleasant.

But all machines use some type of energy. (See page 76 for types of energy.) The energy used to operate a machine is called the **input** or **effort**. The power that comes out is called the **output**, and it often moves a **load.**

Machines that use mechanisms

> **Think about**
>
> - What is a mechanism?
> - What is a machine?
> - What is the difference between input and output?
> - What is the connection between energy, force and work?

> Energy is the ability to do work (see page 76).

Fig. 3 The outline of a car's engine and mechanisms

Mechanisms and motion

Fig. 4 Four simple types of motion

Mechanisms use or create motion.

You might already know of the four kinds of motion listed below. But you may need to learn their technical names.

- **linear** motion — means movement in a straight line.
- **rotary** motion — means a circular movement.
- **oscillating** motion — means a rocking motion back and forth that follows a curve (like a swing).
- **reciprocating** motion — means a to and fro movement in a straight line.

Fig. 5 Model funfair

The six 'simple machines'

There are six basic mechanisms which are called **simple machines.**
They are simply devices that use an effort (energy) to move a load.

1 A **lever** is usually a straight bar with a **pivot** point (turning point) called the **fulcrum**.
2 A **wheel and axle** uses a wheel to turn and lift a load along a certain distance.
3 A **pulley** is a grooved wheel used to move a load or change the direction of a force.
4 The **inclined plane** is a smooth slope used to move a load to a higher place.
5 The **wedge** is a tapered shape which can apply or resist force.
6 The **screw thread** is an inclined plane (a slope) wrapped around a cylinder. The shape that this makes is called a **helix**.

You may want to add further interest by using electronics — see page 68.

Things You Will Try

In this toy funfair you will see examples of the simple machines.

- How many other mechanisms can you see?
- Using this as a start, design your own imaginative toy playground. Try to use a variety of mechanical parts.

Cams

A **cam** is a mechanism that is used to change the form of motion, e.g. from rotary to reciprocating motion (to and fro). It is usually a shaped piece of material that is fitted to a rotating axle (a **shaft**). The cam is normally used with a **follower**. A follower rests on the edge of the cam and as the axle is turned the follower is made to move up and down.

Many machines which use reciprocating motion will have cams inside them. There are several types of cams but those that you will find most useful when you are planning project work are *rotary* and *linear* cams.

● This rotary cam makes the follower *rise* and *fall*.
● The linear cam changes the direction of the reciprocating motion.

Cam profiles

The shape of the cam will make the follower move smoothly or in an irregular motion — see Fig. 7.

heart-shaped   lift cam   four lift cam

Fig. 7 Cam shapes

Circular cams may be used with the hole for the axle not in the centre. This is called an **eccentric** cam — see Fig. 8.

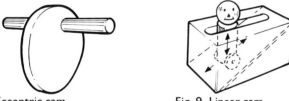

Fig. 8 Eccentric cam   Fig. 9 Linear cam

The part of the cam which makes the follower move upwards is called the **rise**. The part of the cam which makes the follower move down is known as the **fall** — see Fig. 6.

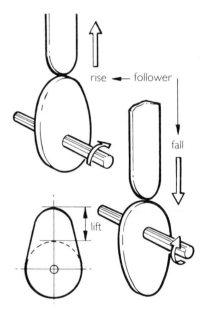

rise ◄— follower

fall

lift

Fig. 6 A simple cam shape showing rise, fall and lift

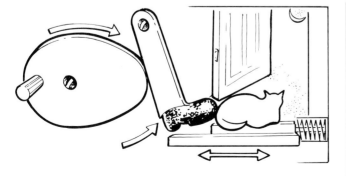

Fig. 10 'Fun board' using cam

Things You Will Try

● Make a single-lift cam — see Fig. 7.
● Make cardboard models of the three cams in Fig. 7. When you understand the different movements, use one or more to move a fun device.
● Sketch some examples of machines that use cams.

Cranks

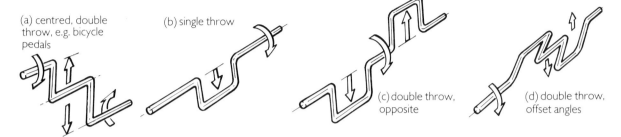

The **crank** is based on the simple machine of the wheel and axle. The **throw** of the crank is the difference in height between the bent part (usually a right angled bend) and the axle that moves around.

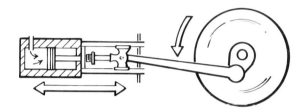

(a) centred, double throw, e.g. bicycle pedals

(b) single throw

(c) double throw, opposite

(d) double throw, offset angles

Fig. 11 Types of crank

The crank is used to change circular motion into reciprocal motion and vice versa.

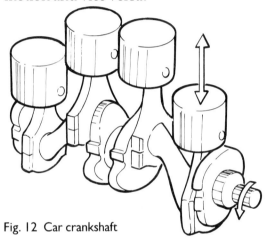

Fig. 12 Car crankshaft

Fig. 13 Steam engine crank

Using cams and cranks in projects

These examples show some of the many ways in which movement can be used in a project. Often a fun idea makes it more interesting!

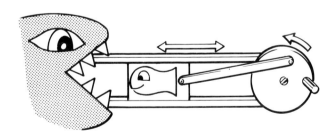

A steam train uses a piston to drive the wheels

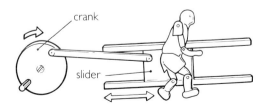

crank

slider

Fig. 14 'Funboard' using crank and slider

Things You Will Try

- Make a single throw crank — see Fig. 11.
- Make a crank and slider — for further details see *Fun Board*, pages 62–63.
- Sketch some examples of devices that use various types of cranks.

Gears

About gears

Gears are wheels with toothed edges. The shape of the tooth can be different depending on the job that it has to do.

You can make simple gears yourself by using a variety of materials — see Fig. 15. It depends on the project.

However, it is difficult to make gears accurately. The manufactured gear wheels that are used in machinery are made very accurately. These are called **precision made** gears.

The most commonly-used type of gear is the **spur gear** which has straight teeth cut *parallel* to the shaft.

Fig. 15 Homemade gear wheels

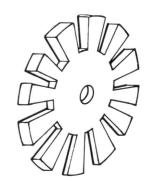

cut out shape

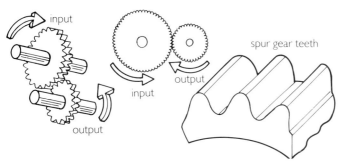

Fig. 16 Spur gears

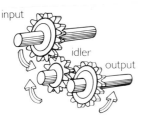

Fig. 17 Gear train

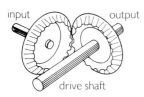

Fig. 18 Bevel gears

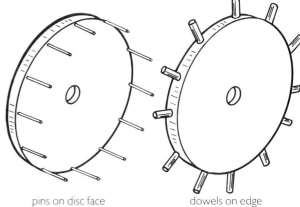

pins on disc face   dowels on edge

What gears do

Gears can be used directly to move a mechanism. They can also be used to change the speed and direction in which something turns.

Sometimes they are also used to change the angle of motion — Fig. 18.

Gear trains

When two or more gears are used together they are called a **gear train**. You will see that when two gear wheels are meshed together, they will turn in opposite directions — Fig. 16.

For two gear wheels to rotate in the same direction a third gear wheel called an **idler** must be placed in the gear train — Fig. 17.

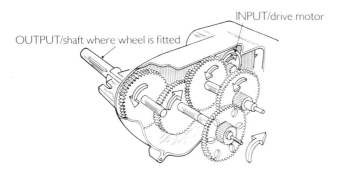

Fig. 19 Gears from 'Big Trak' toy

> ### Think about
> - What do gears do?
> - Where would you use a gear rather than a pulley?
> - If a small gear is driving a larger gear, which would rotate the fastest?

Pulleys

About pulleys

A **pulley** is a wheel that turns on an axle. The wheel usually has a groove in the rim in which the rope or belt can run. The shape of the belt may be flat or vee-shaped. You can make pulley wheels more easily than gear wheels because they are a simpler shape.

What pulleys do

Pulleys can be used to transfer power from one axle to another in forward or reverse, or vary the speed between the axles.

They can also be used to lift heavy loads — see Fig. 27.

Fig. 20 Simple plywood pulley

Making a simple pulley

● Plywood is a good material to use.
● Cut three discs using a hole saw cutter.
● Glue the discs together and hold with a nut and bolt until set — see Fig. 21.

By using more discs you can make up a 'multiple' pulley — see Fig. 22.

Fig. 21 Parts for a simple pulley

Fig. 22 Multiple pulley

Fig. 23 2 pulley wheels, straight belt

axle

Fig. 24 2 pulley wheels, crossed belt

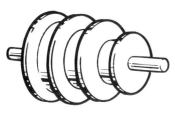

Fig. 25 Different size pulleys

toothed belts on pulleys give non-slip

drive motor

Fig. 26 Pulleys in a food mixer

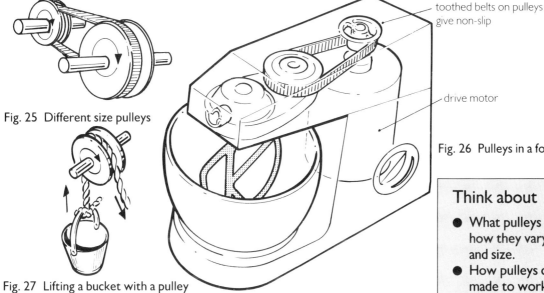

Fig. 27 Lifting a bucket with a pulley

Think about

● What pulleys do and how they vary in shape and size.
● How pulleys can be made to work in different ways.
● Why many machines use pulleys rather than gears.

Gears and pulleys are important devices for making things move in projects.

Levers

About levers

Pole vaulter

You saw a lever on page 81 as a simple machine. All levers have a **fulcrum**, a **load** and an **effort**.

Levers can be made to do different jobs. This depends on where you place the effort when you are moving a load. Usually a lever allows you to use less effort (energy) to move a load. But this means that you have to move the lever a long distance to move the load a little way.

You can increase *leverage* by having the fulcrum or pivot nearer the load — Fig. 28.

The modern pole vaulter uses the leverage of the long and flexible pole to reach great heights. A pole vaulter also uses the natural leverage of the arms to swing over the bar.

Types of lever

There are three types of lever that you will generally use. These are called the **classes** of lever. Each class of lever has the fulcrum, effort and load arranged in a different way.

Class 1 lever
This is the simplest and most common type of lever, in which the pivot or fulcrum is somewhere between the two ends.

Class 2 lever
Here the load is held between the fulcrum and the effort.
You need more force to make this lever work than a class 1 lever.

Class 3 lever
Here the effort is made between the fulcrum and the load.
This needs the most effort to make it work.

Fig. 28 Seesaw as a lever

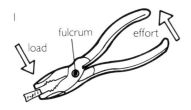
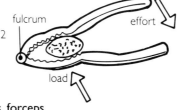
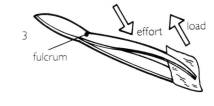
Fig. 29 3 classes of lever: pliers, nutcrackers, forceps

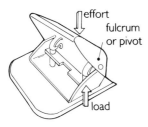
Fig. 30 Paper punch

Things You Will Try

● Make a simple model to demonstrate the three classes of lever.
● Make sketches of four levers that you can find that you may use around the home.

Linkages

A **linkage** is made by connecting two or more levers together.

What linkages do

- Linkages can change the direction of a force or motion.
- They can make objects move parallel to each other or they can make several things move at once.

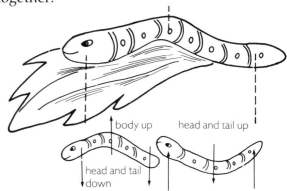

body up   head and tail up

head and tail down

Fig. 31 Model caterpillar

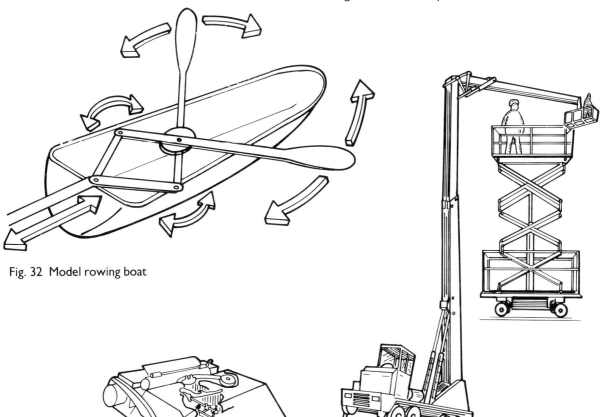

Fig. 32 Model rowing boat

Fig. 33 Typewriter mechanism uses a 'bell crank'

pivot   bell crank

Fig. 34 Hydraulic platforms (a) lever arm, (b) scissors arm

Things You Will Try

- Make a simple cardboard model of a lever and linkage mechanism, such as a human arm or a mechanical excavator.
- Investigate and collect photographs of six interesting devices that use levers and linkages.

The *Fun board* project, page 60, shows you ideas for using mechanisms.

Why use mechanisms?

Often the purpose of mechanisms is to make things easier.

If we use a small effort to move a large load we have made things easier for ourselves. This is an advantage. When we are talking about mechanisms, this advantage is called **mechanical advantage**.

A simple formula to use is:

$$\text{Mechanical Advantage (MA)} = \frac{\text{load}}{\text{effort}}$$

LOAD

EFFORT

Fig. 35 Mechanical advantage using a pulley

Fig. 36 Using a lever makes work easier

Fig. 37 A very long lever could even things out!

In any projects that you make that use mechanisms, you should think about the efficiency of the mechanisms — that is how well they perform. See the *Energy* section, page 76.

Fig. 38 Mechanical levers make work easier!

Things You Will Try

Devise mechanisms that will make the robot in Fig. 39 work.

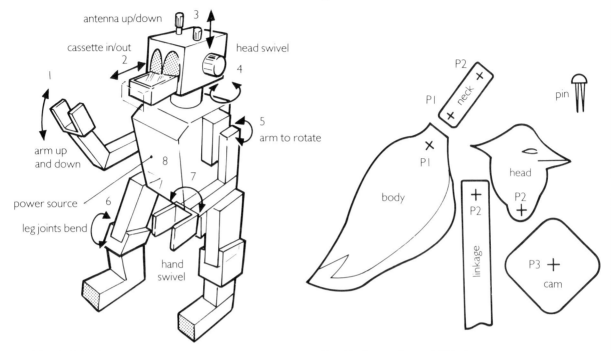

Fig. 39 Model robot

Fig. 40 Parts of a model bird

With cardboard modelling you can work out the sizes of parts for a design — see Fig. 40. Try the idea shown and design one of your own based on animals, figures or vehicles.

Fig. 41 'Heath Robinson' style waking up machine

Waking up can be difficult. Fig. 41 shows an invention to wake you up and make breakfast! Try your own ideas, or make a device for getting up and down stairs, or for painting a room, or for delivering letters.

Structures

About structures

A simple way to think about structures is as frames and shells. A **frame** has many single parts linked together. A **shell** looks like one whole piece.

Structures can be natural or made by people.

SHELLS

FRAME

Fig. 1 Breakfast table and items all have a structure

Look at Fig. 1 which shows a breakfast table. Make a list of the frames and shells that you can see.

The large structures made by people have always left a clear mark on the landscape. With the advance of technology this is even more evident today.

Structures are universal because they make the *support* or *construction* of all the things that we see and use.

The flat or house you live in is a structure. All the items that you use everyday have some form of structure — even *you* are a structure!

Fig. 2 Selection of structures made by people

Natural structures

Nature has provided us with good examples of specialised structures. Each structure has a purpose. The tortoise has a strong shell for protection. The tree has a branch (a frame) to help the leaves spread out to catch the sunlight, and roots to help give support to the upper structure of branches.

By looking around you carefully and by investigating your ideas, you may find a starting point for the structure of a design of your own.

Fig. 3 Selection of animals

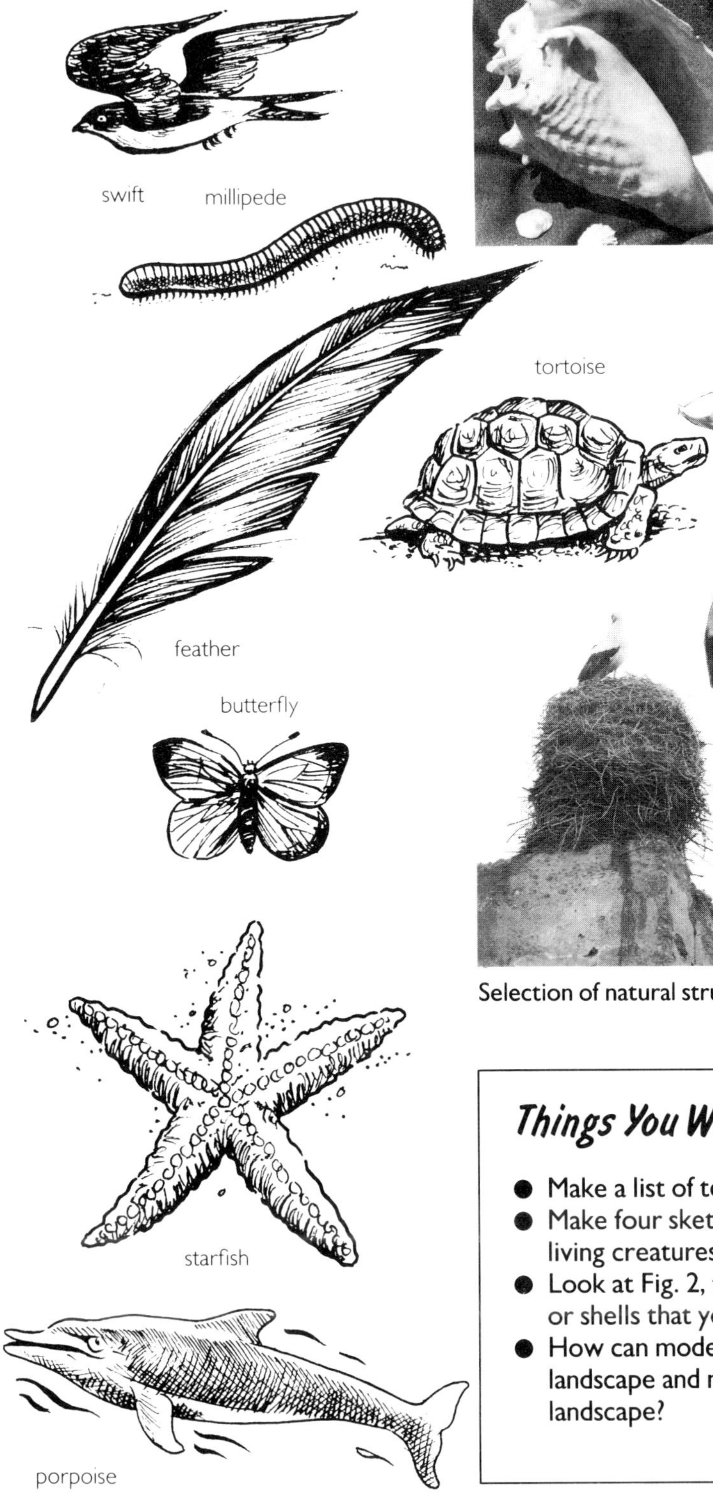

swift

millipede

feather

tortoise

butterfly

Selection of natural structures

starfish

porpoise

Things You Will Try

- Make a list of ten natural structures, and sketch them.
- Make four sketches of your own choice showing specialised living creatures.
- Look at Fig. 2, the large drawing, and make a list of the frames or shells that you can see.
- How can modern society make its structures *blend* with the landscape and not be out of keeping, ugly or damaging to the landscape?

Making structures

Shapes soon grow to make
structures.

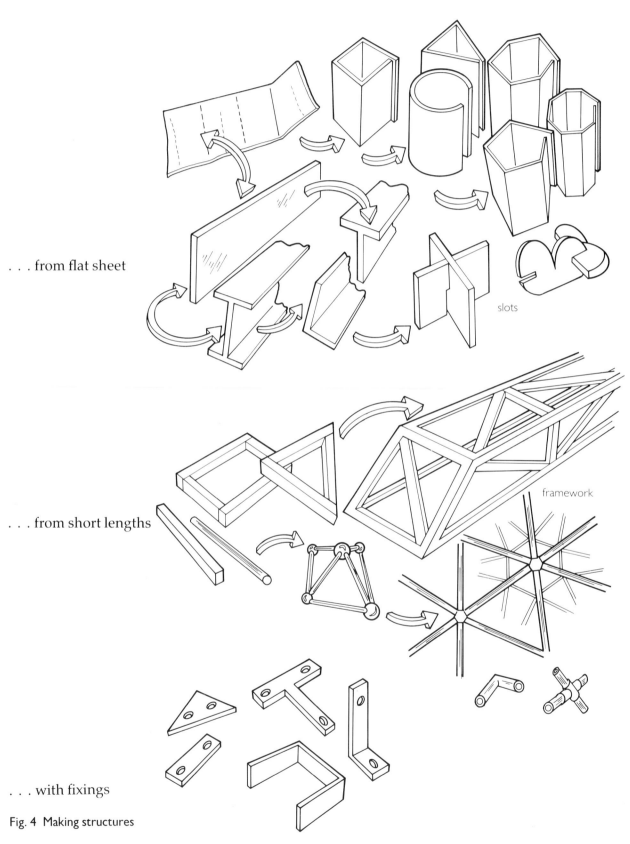

. . . from flat sheet

slots

. . . from short lengths

framework

. . . with fixings

Fig. 4 Making structures

For help with modelling your structures, see *Design Process*,
page 14.

Things You Will Try

1 Design and make a simple construction kit for a young child. The pieces should be made from flat sheet and they should fix together using slots. You need make only a few sample pieces, say, up to ten.

Some considerations:

- size of pieces
- shape
- number of slots
- method of fixing
- colour, pattern or texture
- versatility

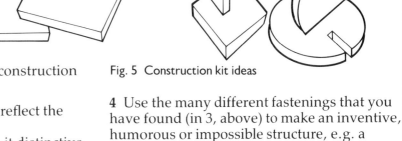

Fig. 5 Construction kit ideas

2 Make a package to hold your construction kit. It could:

- be an interesting structure to reflect the contents,
- have colour/graphics to make it distinctive,
- give brief instructions.

3 Look at the many ways of joining two materials together, see for example, Fig. 8. Make your own drawings of six methods of joining items. Add a brief description to each idea.

4 Use the many different fastenings that you have found (in 3, above) to make an inventive, humorous or impossible structure, e.g. a shoelace bridge! Sketch your ideas in an imaginative way.

5 Look at and investigate the many different types of bridges. Make models of two different kinds of bridge to span a distance of 300 mm. Test the strength of each bridge by hanging weights on it.
(a) Use a framework structure made up from short lengths, or a construction kit.
(b) Use parts that are pulled together by string or elastic.

6 Design a storage box system to be made in plastic. Make a 'prototype' model to show how similar boxes can fit together — Fig. 6.

7 Design a baby buggy using a scale model — Fig. 7.

Some considerations:

- You should use a framework.
- The buggy should fold up for storage.
- There should be a safe seating area.
- There could be a storage area.
- The wheels must be easy to steer and lock.

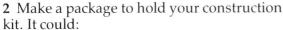
area which can grip

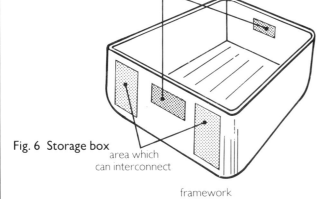

Fig. 6 Storage box
area which can interconnect

framework

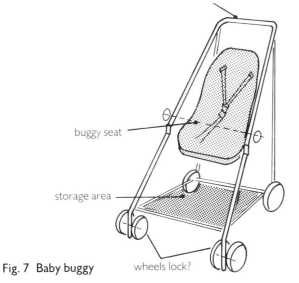

buggy seat

storage area

Fig. 7 Baby buggy
wheels lock?

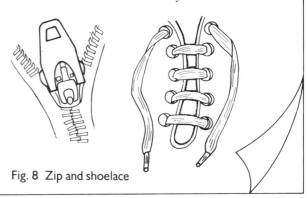

Fig. 8 Zip and shoelace

Pneumatics

About pneumatics

Pumping up a tyre

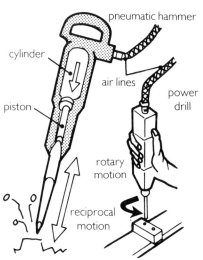

The word **pneumatics** may sound complicated but it means simply the use of wind or air to transfer energy. The energy is used to drive something or make something work.

The air carries energy by being stored under pressure — it is **compressed**. The air is released again by some kind of mechanism. This also releases the energy that has been stored.

When you blow up a balloon or pump up a bicycle tyre, the air is compressed to a low pressure. This means the stored air is always waiting to be released. If the energy in the air is controlled it can be made to do useful work — see Fig. 2.

A bicycle pump is a **pneumatic device**, that is, it can deliver or push air. It is a **'single-acting' cylinder** because the pressure of the air moves the piston down the barrel — a single action. But it needs a spring to return it for the next push or **stroke** — see Fig. 1.

Blowing up a balloon

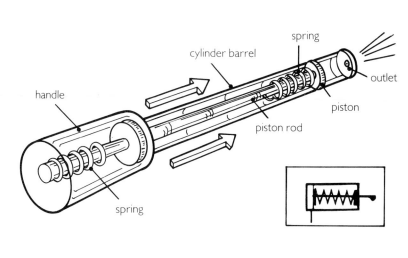

Fig. 1 Bicycle pump and circuit symbol for single-acting cylinder

Fig. 2 Pneumatic drills

Pneumatic power

Pneumatics are often used to drive industrial tools because pneumatic systems are cheap to operate and safe to use — see Fig. 2. The air is delivered at a high pressure by a device called a 'compressor'.

As in electronics, pneumatic devices have special circuit symbols to represent them in diagrams (Fig. 1). This helps a designer to show to others how a system is planned and meant to work.

The devices will be linked together with tubes carrying the air supply (like the wires in an electronic circuit). The air in the tubes is usually under pressure. When the air has been used it is said to **exhaust**. It is usually recycled, that is used again, through an **air reservoir** or **compressor**.

Using pneumatics

This school-built robot arm — 'Boris' — shows some of the simple movements that can be powered by pneumatics – Fig 3.

The arm has also been linked to a computer. This means that a series of commands for movement can be given, and remembered. These can then be repeated as many times as required.

 See the *Computer* section, page 72 for simple help with computer control.

To be able to operate accurately many times, the robot arm uses industrial quality parts. These are made very precisely so that they behave in the same way each time.

The pneumatic cylinders in the robot arm are **double-acting**. This means they both push and pull. (Compare this with the single-acting bicycle pump.)

The cylinders are also linked to special **valves** which control the air supply. These are electrically operated so that the computer can send signals to turn them ON or OFF.

Fig. 3 Pneumatic robot arm

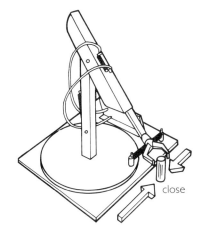

close

turn

lift

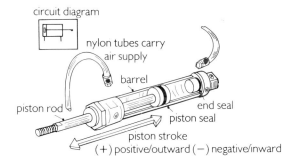

```
CONTROL LEARNING PROGRAM


Begin now.....


? 1
? 5
? 7
? 0


Your program is.....

Grab closed for 11 secs
Grab closed/base turns for 6 secs
Grab/arm and base for 3 secs
```

```
BORIS bids you welcome.....
You may control me by pressing
the following keys:-

1 - close grab

2 - move arm

3 - arm/grab closed

4 - turn base

5 - grab and turn

6 - arm and turn

7 - all combined

0 - stop

I will memorize your actions
and then replay them.
```

Fig. 4 Part of computer program to control robot

Fig. 5 Part of computer display for robot program

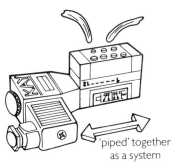

'piped' together as a system

Fig. 6 5-port solenoid valve

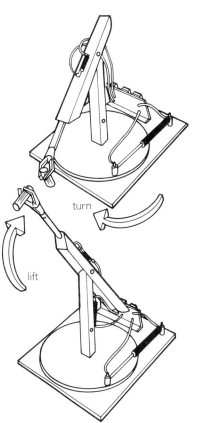

circuit diagram

nylon tubes carry air supply

barrel

piston rod

end seal

piston seal

piston stroke
(+) positive/outward (−) negative/inward

Fig. 7 Double-acting cylinder and symbol

Low-pressure uses

The introductory pages have shown you how pneumatics are an important power source if they use high-pressure air movement. But you can also use low-pressure air movement.

Here are some ideas and methods for using simple low-pressure air movement to create moving parts in projects.

You can use:

- a plastic container (air reservoir) and a balloon.
- a simple syringe used as a piston.

These can be used with other mechanical parts — see *Mechanisms*, page 80.

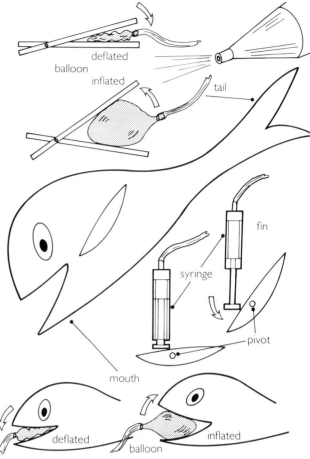

Fig. 8 Ideas for using balloon to animate model whale

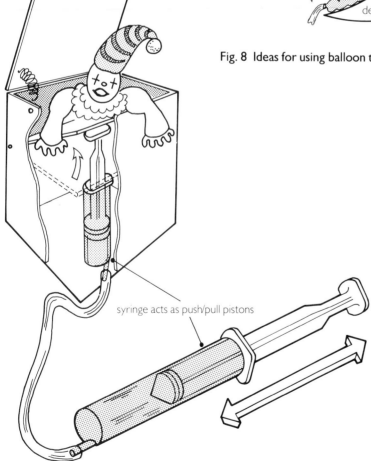

Fig. 9 Julie made her 'jack-in-box' activate using pneumatics

Make your own piston

You can make your own piston using a small empty plastic tube, discs and short rods.

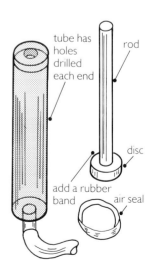

Fig. 10 Making a piston

Things You Will Try

1 If you have a kit like 'Lego' Pneumatics, make a simple holding device. You can add your own made-up parts to ordinary 'Lego' or other constructional kit.

2 Make a model of an animal, real, imaginary, or prehistoric. Use pneumatics to make the parts move. For example, the gripper shown in Fig. 12 could be used as a mouth for the model.

How would you move a tail or wings?

3 Link a crank to a pneumatic cylinder to turn rotary motion into reciprocating motion (to and fro).

Use this pneumatic mechanism to move a humorous model, a nursery rhyme scene or a cartoon character.

4 Using a balloon, design and make a lift that can stop at three different levels. The levels must be the same distance apart.

5 Make an amusing face that has parts which are moved by different simple pneumatic devices.

6 Make a simple sweet dispenser that can deliver three different chocloate bars. Use a combination of pneumatic and mechanical parts.

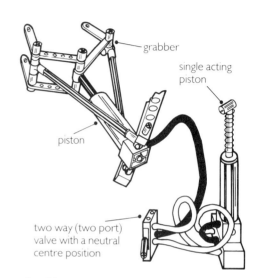

Fig. 11 Lego pneumatics kit

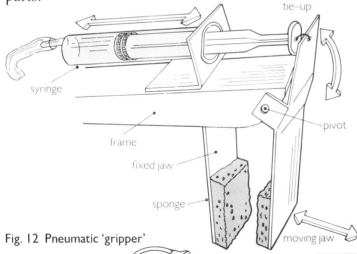

Fig. 12 Pneumatic 'gripper'

 ── *Safety* ──

The syringes shown are non-medical and safe to use, but:

● take care not to puncture the skin.
● never use pneumatics near eyes.
● never place syringes inside ears or nose.

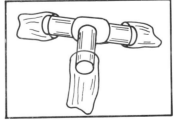

Fig. 13 T-junction

 # Beginning to make

About making

Having designed your project and had it checked by your teacher, you are now ready to make your final design.

 Have you understood all the *requirements* of the project? If not, refer to the *Design process* section, page 6. Remember that time spent on design solves problems at the making stage.

A guide to the making process

Marking out
- guide? accuracy? size?

Material
- type? size? appearance?

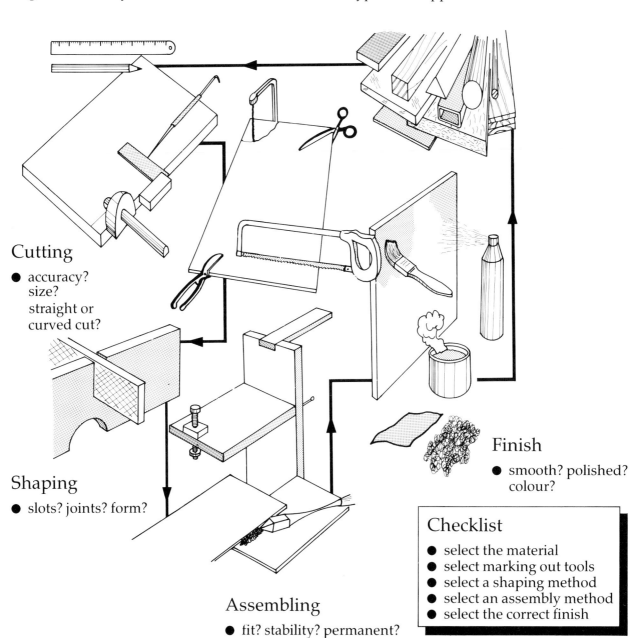

Cutting
- accuracy?
  size?
  straight or
  curved cut?

Shaping
- slots? joints? form?

Finish
- smooth? polished? colour?

Checklist
- select the material
- select marking out tools
- select a shaping method
- select an assembly method
- select the correct finish

Assembling
- fit? stability? permanent?

Selecting the material

You will need to think carefully about what material to use in your project.

The final choice will depend upon:

- what is available
- the cost
- the stock sizes (this means the available sizes)
- the ease of working
- the look and use of it
- the right material for the job
- how well it will last

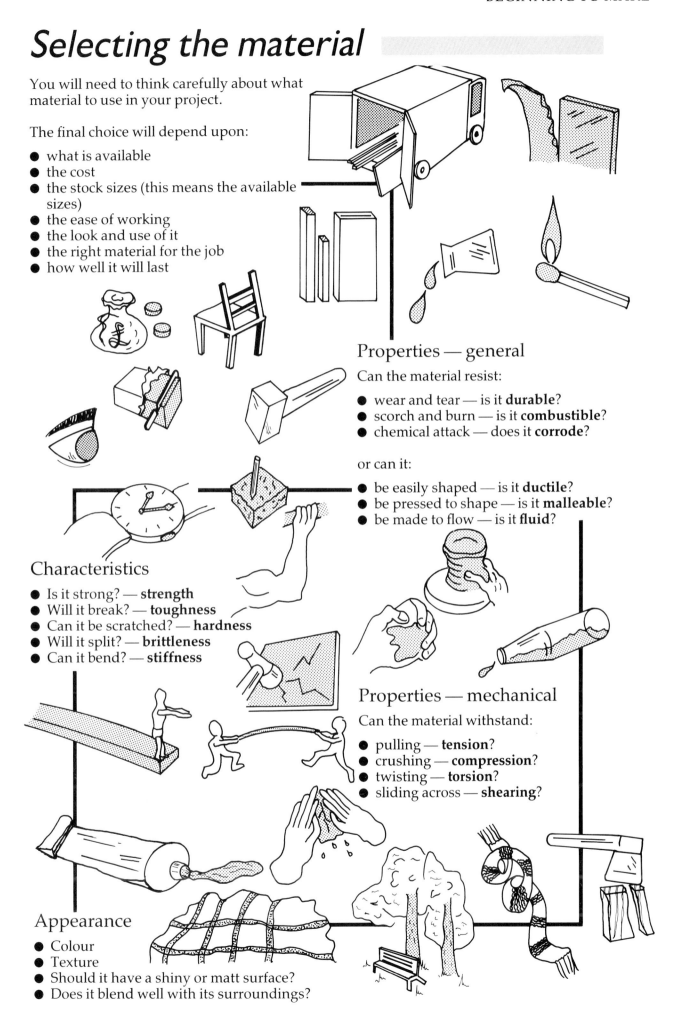

Properties — general

Can the material resist:

- wear and tear — is it **durable**?
- scorch and burn — is it **combustible**?
- chemical attack — does it **corrode**?

or can it:

- be easily shaped — is it **ductile**?
- be pressed to shape — is it **malleable**?
- be made to flow — is it **fluid**?

Characteristics

- Is it strong? — **strength**
- Will it break? — **toughness**
- Can it be scratched? — **hardness**
- Will it split? — **brittleness**
- Can it bend? — **stiffness**

Properties — mechanical

Can the material withstand:

- pulling — **tension**?
- crushing — **compression**?
- twisting — **torsion**?
- sliding across — **shearing**?

Appearance

- Colour
- Texture
- Should it have a shiny or matt surface?
- Does it blend well with its surroundings?

Common materials

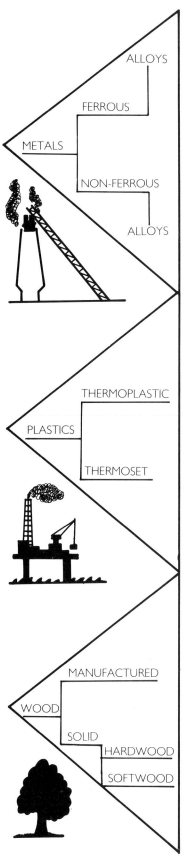

TYPE	IDENTIFICATION	USES	PROPERTIES
Mild steel	smooth grey surface	general constructions	strong, hard and ductile
Tin plate (coated steel)	shiny, silvery surface	sheet and box constructions	easy to form
Aluminium	silver grey, lightweight	casting, tube or sheet	easy to cut and work
Copper	golden reddish, shiny	tube and sheet	easy to work, solders well
Brass	golden yellowish, quite heavy	solid bar, tube and sheet	harder to cut, can be soldered
Acrylic	hard, smooth, lightweight	general purposes	brittle, easy to scratch
Polystyrene	soft and flexible	suitable for vacuum forming	forms easily
Polyester Resin			
Unreinforced	clear and liquid	encapsulated castings	hard and brittle
Reinforced	matted surface	continuous shell-like shapes	light with some flexibility
Chipboard	compressed particles	use as core over large areas	heavy and brittle
Plywood	three or more layers	general use over an area	strong and easy to shape
Abura	pinkish and plain surface	general purpose	easy to work
Mahogany	reddish-brown, attractive grain	framework	can blunt cutting tools quickly
Whitewood	creamy white	general construction	easy to work
Pine	Yellowish white, resinous	general construction	easy to work, can have many knots

Commonly-available sections

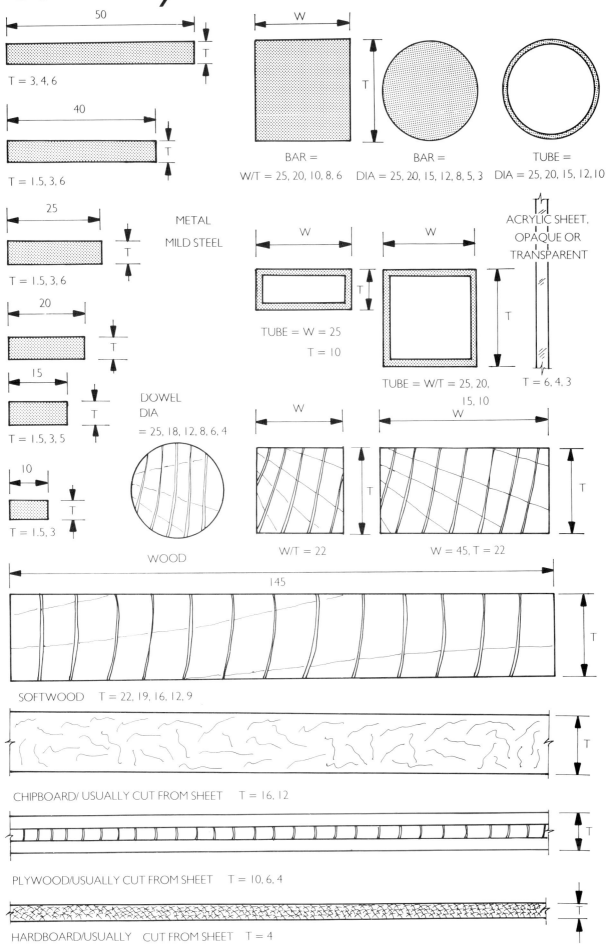

50

T = 3, 4, 6

40

T = 1.5, 3, 6

25

T = 1.5, 3, 6

20

T = 1.5, 3, 6

15

T = 1.5, 3, 5

10

T = 1.5, 3

METAL

MILD STEEL

W

T

BAR =
W/T = 25, 20, 10, 8, 6

BAR =
DIA = 25, 20, 15, 12, 8, 5, 3

TUBE =
DIA = 25, 20, 15, 12, 10

W

T

TUBE = W = 25
T = 10

W

T

TUBE = W/T = 25, 20,
15, 10

ACRYLIC SHEET,
OPAQUE OR
TRANSPARENT

T

T = 6, 4, 3

DOWEL
DIA
= 25, 18, 12, 8, 6, 4

WOOD

W

T

W/T = 22

W

T

W = 45, T = 22

145

T

SOFTWOOD   T = 22, 19, 16, 12, 9

T

CHIPBOARD/ USUALLY CUT FROM SHEET   T = 16, 12

T

PLYWOOD/USUALLY CUT FROM SHEET   T = 10, 6, 4

T

HARDBOARD/USUALLY   CUT FROM SHEET   T = 4

ALL MEASUREMENTS IN MILLIMETRES

Marking out

Why marking out?

Marking out is necessary if you are to achieve an **accurate** result and avoid **wasting** material. During the making stages of your projects, good marking out is very important.

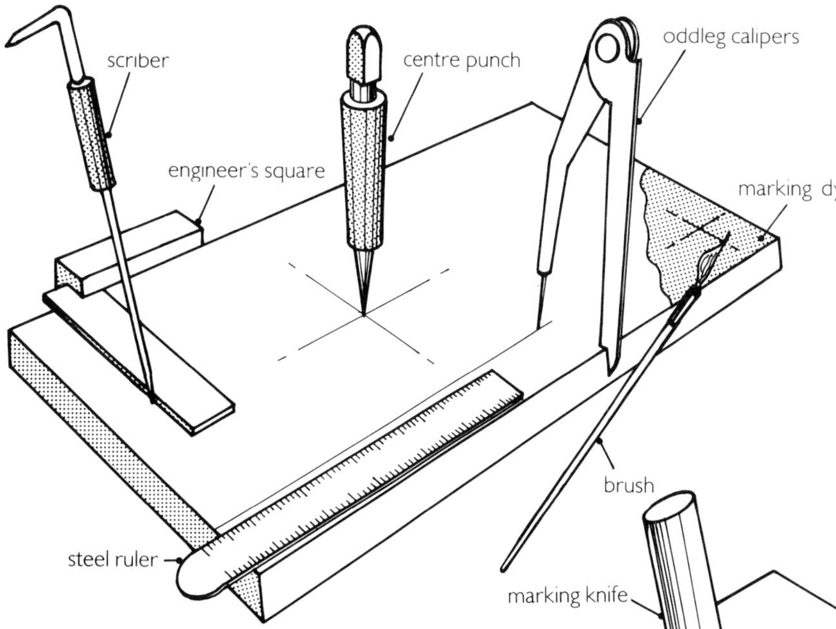

Fig. 1 Tools for marking out on metal

labels: scriber, engineer's square, centre punch, oddleg calipers, marking dye, brush, steel ruler

Using tools

The tools in use today were originally made for use with a particular material. Many design projects now use a mixture of materials, so tools are used in a wider range of ways.

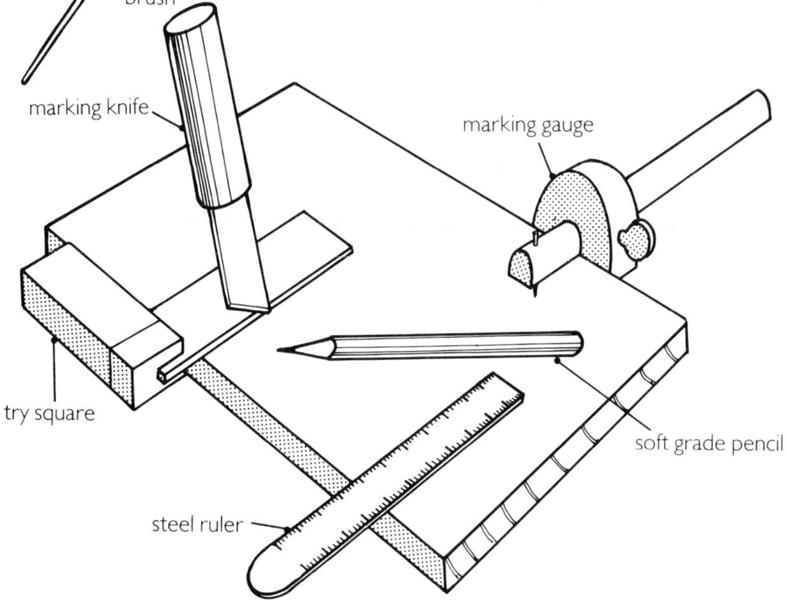

Fig. 2 Tools for marking out on wood

labels: marking knife, marking gauge, try square, soft grade pencil, steel ruler

Specific points

- A steel rule is very accurate and with it you can measure directly from one end. You can also use it to check how level a piece of material is.
- A square allows you to draw accurate lines at 90° to a straight edge.
- The marking knife and scriber score a line into the material.
- A pencil or spirit pen mark only the surface.
- The marking gauge and calipers allow you to draw parallel lines.

Checklist   ✓̲ *main use*   ✓ *other use*   ✗ *not used*

Material	Marking dye	Scriber	Steel rule	Engineer's square	Centre punch	Odd-leg calipers	Pencil	Marking knife	Try square	Marking gauge	Spirit-based pen
Metal	✓̲	✓̲	✓̲	✓̲	✓̲	✓̲	✗	✗	✓	✗	✓
Plastic	✗	✓	✓̲	✓	✗	✓	✓	✗	✓	✗	✓̲
Wood	✗	✗	✓̲	✓	✗	✗	✓̲	✓̲	✓̲	✓̲	✗

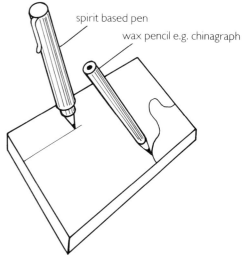

Fig. 3 Tools for marking out on plastic

labels: spirit based pen, wax pencil e.g. chinagraph

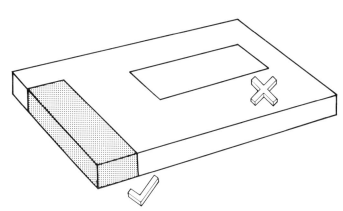

Fig. 4 Cutting to avoid waste

Care in marking out

Materials are **expensive**. It is important to think about how and where you mark out on the material.

Try to position the piece that you require so that cutting it out wastes as little of the material as possible — see Fig. 4.

Finding the centre

● The centre square helps you to find the centre of a round piece of material.
● Drawing in the diagonals helps you to find the centre on a piece of rectangular material.

Circles and arcs

These can be marked out using compasses. Use a pencil for wood and a spirit pen for plastic. For metal, the spring dividers will score on the surface.

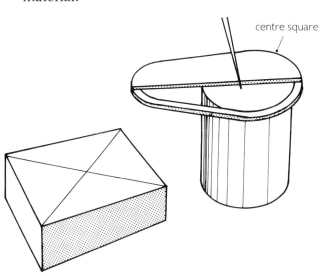

Fig. 5 Finding the centre

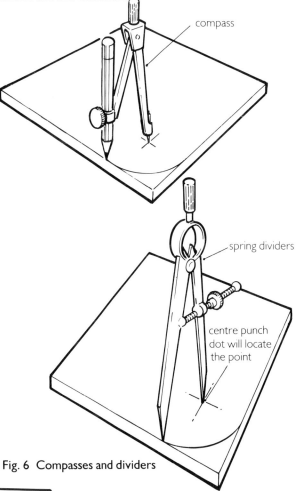

Fig. 6 Compasses and dividers

Complex shapes

If you have a complex design, or if you need to repeat your design several times, you will find a **template** useful. The material that the template is made from will depend on how it is to be used.

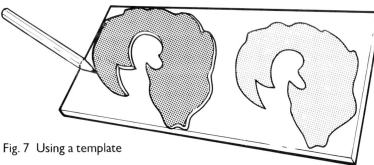

Fig. 7 Using a template

Cutting

Making straight cuts

Cutting a material to length, shape or size is a process that you will often need to do. Whatever the material, you should follow this procedure.

● Marking out should be clear and accurate.
● Hold the work firmly, e.g. in a vice.
● Place the cutting line close to where the material is held.
● Cut on the waste side and begin by drawing the saw towards you.
● Use a smooth action and the full length of the blade.

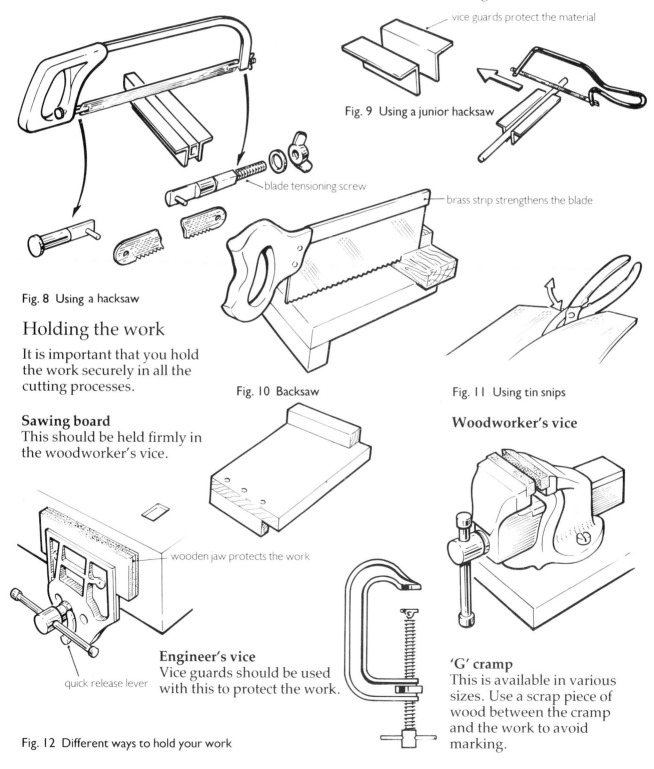

vice guards protect the material

Fig. 9 Using a junior hacksaw

blade tensioning screw

brass strip strengthens the blade

Fig. 8 Using a hacksaw

Holding the work

It is important that you hold the work securely in all the cutting processes.

Fig. 10 Backsaw

Fig. 11 Using tin snips

Sawing board
This should be held firmly in the woodworker's vice.

Woodworker's vice

wooden jaw protects the work

Engineer's vice
Vice guards should be used with this to protect the work.

quick release lever

Fig. 12 Different ways to hold your work

'G' cramp
This is available in various sizes. Use a scrap piece of wood between the cramp and the work to avoid marking.

Cutting curves

The blades in these tools are fine so that you can cut curves. They are easily broken. You should take **care** when you are using them.

The abrafile

The abrafile can be used to follow the line of a disc in metal or plastic.

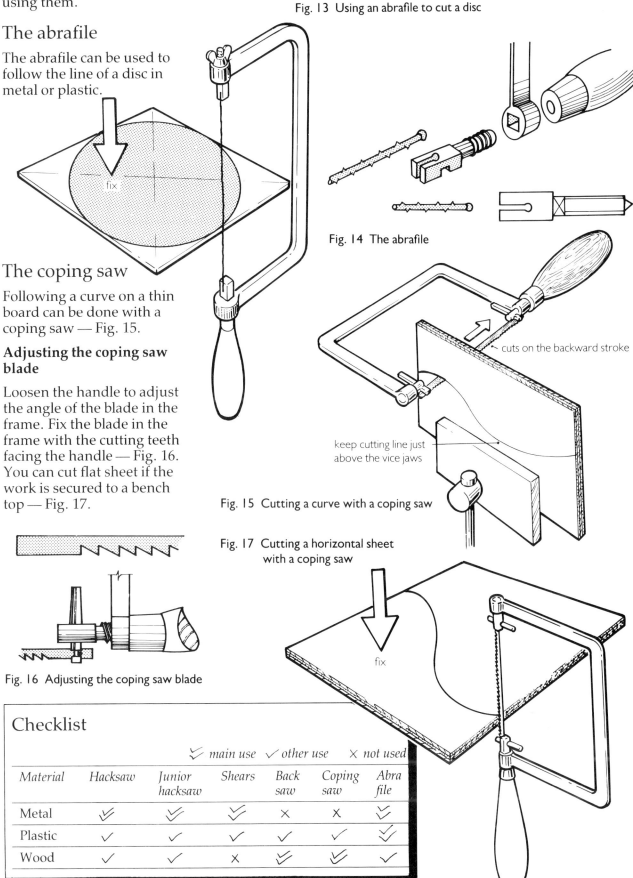

Fig. 13 Using an abrafile to cut a disc

fix

Fig. 14 The abrafile

The coping saw

Following a curve on a thin board can be done with a coping saw — Fig. 15.

Adjusting the coping saw blade

Loosen the handle to adjust the angle of the blade in the frame. Fix the blade in the frame with the cutting teeth facing the handle — Fig. 16. You can cut flat sheet if the work is secured to a bench top — Fig. 17.

← cuts on the backward stroke

keep cutting line just above the vice jaws

Fig. 15 Cutting a curve with a coping saw

Fig. 17 Cutting a horizontal sheet with a coping saw

fix

Fig. 16 Adjusting the coping saw blade

Checklist

			⋎ main use	✓ other use	✕ not used	
Material	Hacksaw	Junior hacksaw	Shears	Back saw	Coping saw	Abra file
Metal	⋎	⋎	⋎	✕	✕	⋎
Plastic	✓	✓	✓	✓	✓	⋎
Wood	✓	✓	✕	⋎	⋎	✓

Drilling: by hand

At some point when making your design you will need to make a hole. The method you use will depend on the size of the hole that you need and the equipment that is available.

The bradawl

The bradawl is the simplest way of making a small hole in wood. It is useful for making a 'starter' hole for screws.

The hand drill

For drilling small holes up to 8 mm diameter in wood, plastic and thin metal you can use a hand drill. It uses bits called **twist drills**. You should turn the handle in a clockwise direction whilst applying a downward pressure when drilling a hole. Check regularly that you are drilling an accurate hole to the size that you have chosen. Take care that the drill has not 'wandered' to one side.

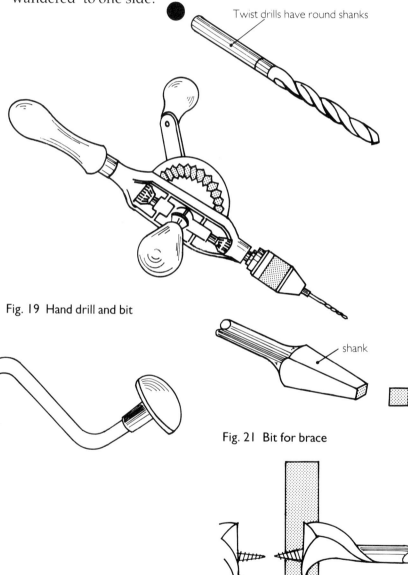

Twist drills have round shanks

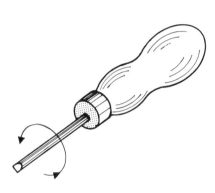

Fig. 18 Bradawl

The carpenter's brace

When you need to make larger holes in wood you can use a carpenter's brace.

Fig. 19 Hand drill and bit

shank

Fig. 21 Bit for brace

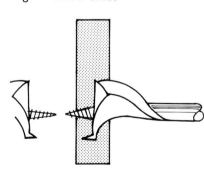

Fig. 22 Preventing wood splitting when drilling

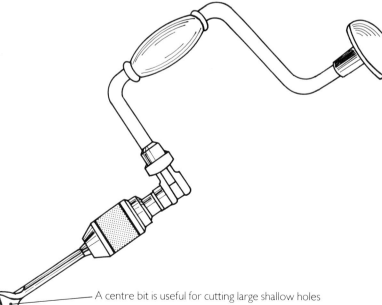

A centre bit is useful for cutting large shallow holes

Fig. 20 Carpenter's brace and bit

When you are using a carpenter's brace, you can stop the wood splitting by boring through the wood until the point of the bit shows through the other side. Then turn the work round and bore the rest of the hole.

Drilling: by machine

The **drilling machine** makes it easier to drill holes, especially when you have a lot to do. As long as your work is held securely on the machine table you will be able to drill holes accurately. Different drilling speeds can be used when necessary.

Fig. 23 Drilling machine

Always wear safety goggles

Electric hand drill

The chuck key tightens the drill in place (do not leave the chuck in)

Fig. 24 Chuck key

Secure the work using the hand or machine vice

Fig. 25 Auger bit

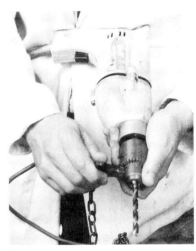

Electric drill — tightening the bit

The power hand drill

This is a quick way of making a hole. You can change the speed of the drill quickly and with little effort.

Twist drills of various sizes are tightened in the chuck by using a **chuck key** — Fig. 24. Always check that the drill you are using is held centrally in the jaws of the chuck and it is held firm.

Fig. 26 Forstner bit

Fig. 27 Countersink drill

Other useful cutting bits

The **auger** bit (Fig. 25) allows deep, straight holes to be cut.

The **Forstner** bit (Fig. 26) cuts a clean hole with a flat bottom.

The **countersink** bit (Fig. 27) cuts a recess that allows a screwhead to be flush with the surface.

The **hole saw cutter** (Fig. 28) allows holes of various sizes to be cut.

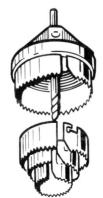

Fig. 28 Hole saw cutter

Checklist

	Bradawl	Centre bit	Countersink drill	Forstner bit	Hole saw cutter	Auger bit	Twist drill
Metal	X	X	✓	X	X	X	✓
Plastic	X	X	✓	X	✓	X	✓
Wood	✓	✓	✓	✓	✓	✓	✓

Shaping material: metal

Files are used to shape metal. They come in different shapes
and sizes. Files can also be used on plastics.

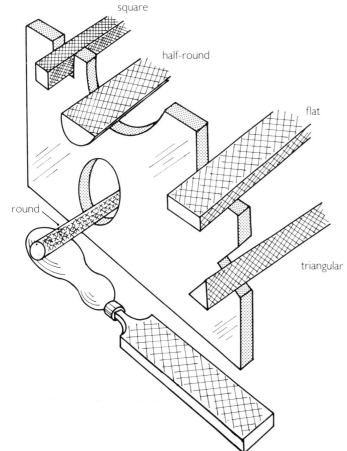

A **square** file is used for grooving and slotting.
A **round** or **rat-tail** file is used to enlarge or
smooth holes.
The **half-round** file is used on concave
surfaces.
The **triangular** or **three-square** file is used to
get into sharp corners.
The **flat** file is used for general bench work.
Cross filing is used to file down to a line.
Draw filing gives a smooth finish to the work.
Flat files usually have one edge without teeth.
This is called a **safe-edge.**

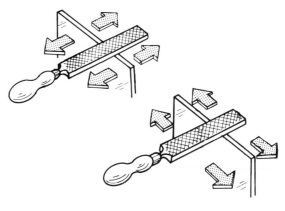

Fig. 29 Types of file

Fig. 30 Cross filing and draw filing

Shaping material: plastics

Remember that many plastics are brittle and will break easily if
they are not well supported. Keep the part that you are filing as
low in the vice as possible. Move the work several times if
necessary.

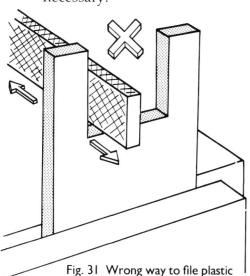

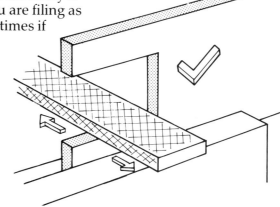

Fig. 32 Right way to file plastic

Keep the paper on the plastic to prevent it from being
scratched while you are filing.

Fig. 31 Wrong way to file plastic

108

Shaping material: wood

Planes

Planing is a quick way of removing waste wood.

A **jack** plane is used for general purpose work.

A **smoothing** plane is used for finishing work, e.g. cleaning a joint before it is glass-papered and varnished. The smoothing plane is similar in shape to the jack plane, but smaller.

As you push the plane forward you must press down at the front.

When planing the end grain of the wood it is best to plane from both ends to the centre. If you plane straight across the end grain, the edge of the wood will split — Fig. 33.

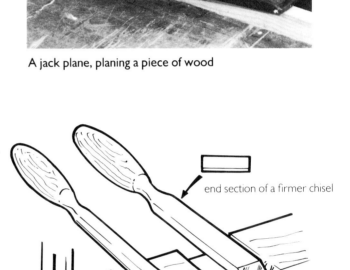

A jack plane, planing a piece of wood

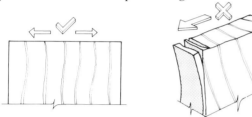

Fig. 33 Right and wrong way to plane end grain of wood

Chisels

Chisels can be used for removing small amounts of waste wood as well as for shaping. A **firmer** chisel is used for general purpose work. A **bevel-edge** chisel is used for getting into awkward corners —
Fig. 34.
Use a wooden mallet to hit the chisel if you cannot push it with your hand.

end section of a firmer chisel

end section of a bevel edge chisel

Fig. 34 Chisels

Surforms

Surforms (Fig. 35) are used for fast removal of wood and are mainly used for shaping curved work. The blade has lots of tiny chisel-like teeth. When the teeth are worn the blade must be replaced by a new one. Blades can be flat, round or half-round.

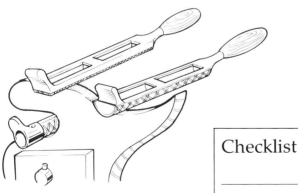

Fig. 35 Surforms

Checklist

	Files	Planes	Chisels	Surforms
Metal	✓	×	×	×
Plastic	✓	∗	×	×
Wood	✓	✓	✓	✓
∗ only for edges				

Shaping material: metal

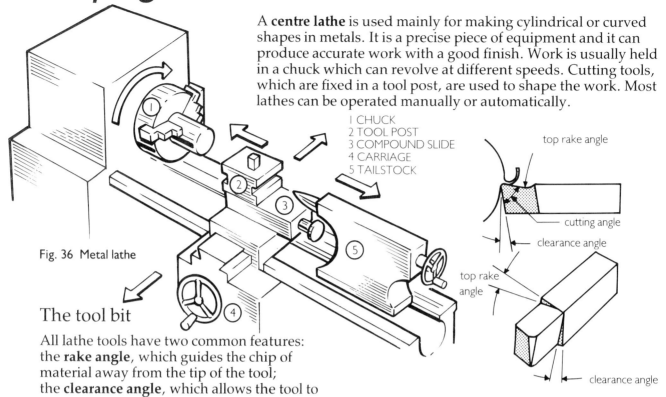

A **centre lathe** is used mainly for making cylindrical or curved shapes in metals. It is a precise piece of equipment and it can produce accurate work with a good finish. Work is usually held in a chuck which can revolve at different speeds. Cutting tools, which are fixed in a tool post, are used to shape the work. Most lathes can be operated manually or automatically.

1 CHUCK
2 TOOL POST
3 COMPOUND SLIDE
4 CARRIAGE
5 TAILSTOCK

Fig. 36 Metal lathe

Fig. 37 Angles of lathe tools

The tool bit

All lathe tools have two common features: the **rake angle**, which guides the chip of material away from the tip of the tool; the **clearance angle**, which allows the tool to cut but not rub against the work.

Common methods of shaping

Most lathe tools are made from **high speed steel**. They are ground to various shapes depending upon the way that they are to be used.

The **knife-tool** reduces the thickness of the workpiece and is useful for giving a sharp corner — Fig. 38.

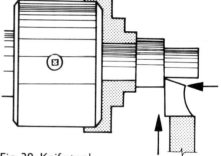

Fig. 38 Knife tool

The **round-nosed tool** will produce a flat surface at right angles to an edge — Fig. 39.

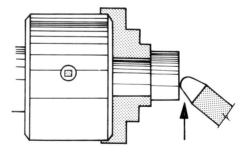

Fig. 39 Round-nosed tool

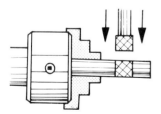

Fig. 40 Knurling tool

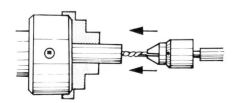

Fig. 41 Drilling on the lathe

Other useful things you can do on a centre lathe

A **knurling tool** cuts a criss-cross pattern which makes the work easier to grip — useful for handles and thumbscrews — Fig. 40.
An accurate hole can be drilled through the workpiece using a **twist drill** held in a chuck on the tailstock — Fig. 41.

Assembling the material: plastic

Many of the mechanical joining methods used for metal can be used on plastics such as acrylic. Care must be taken not to overtighten screws or nuts and bolts, as this will cause certain plastics to crack.

Plastic can be joined to metal using a nut and bolt. A clearance hole should be drilled in both pieces of material.

Plastic can be joined to wood using a wood screw (but not into end grain). A clearance hole should be drilled in the plastic. A pilot hole drilled in the wood will guide the screw.

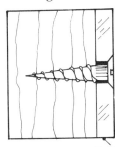

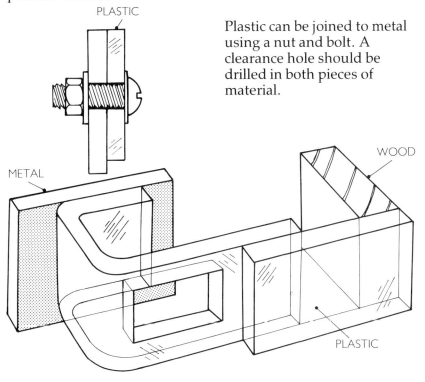

Fig. 42 Joining plastic to wood, metal or plastic

Plastic can be joined to itself by using several methods. It can be glued (1), or held together with a nut and bolt (2), or screwed together with a self-tapping screw (3).

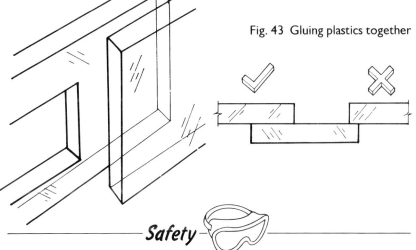

Gluing plastics

Two-part epoxy resin can be used to bond most plastics. The best glue to use on acrylic is 'Tensol' cement.

Hold this joint together until the glue sets.

A better hold is obtained by providing a large gluing area.

Fig. 43 Gluing plastics together

Tensol cement for gluing plastic

'Tensol' is the registered tradename for ICI's cement, specially developed for use with 'Perspex' acrylic sheet. 'Tensol' and 'Perspex' are tradenames, the property of companies within the ICI Group.

Safety

ALWAYS use 'Tensol' cement in a well ventilated area and replace the lid immediately after use.

Assembling the material: metal

The most common way of joining a metal to itself or another metal, or even another material, is by a **mechanical joint**, e.g. an additional fixing such as a nut and bolt. An important factor in helping you decide which fixing to use is whether the joint needs to be permanent or semi-permanent.

Semi-permanent

A variety of metal **screws** can be used. Usually a **clearance hole** will be drilled in the first piece of metal. A smaller hole is drilled in the second which then has a thread tapped in it. Four common types of screws are shown in Fig. 44.

Fig. 44 Types of metal screw

2 Round head — used where it does not matter if the screwhead comes above the surface.

3 Countersunk — used where the screwhead needs to be below the surface.

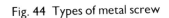
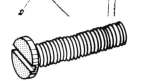

1 Cheesehead — general purpose. Useful for holding thin parts.

4 Grub screw — these are often used to fix a part to a rotating shaft, e.g. a handle. They fit below the surface.

There are various types of screws. The most common you will use in school is metric (M). If you need a metal screw with a diameter of 10 mm you should write down M10. The 'M' stands for metric and the number that follows it is the diameter you require — Fig. 45.

Fig. 45 Metric screw

Self-tapping screws are useful for joining thin metal together, e.g. sheet aluminium. They have a very coarse thread which makes a hold in the material being joined when it is fixed — see Fig. 46.

Washers are often used to protect the surface of the part being joined.

Spring washers can be used underneath the nut to prevent it coming undone — Fig. 47.

Alternatively, a second nut can be 'locked' against the first.

Fig. 46 Self-tapping screw

flat washer   spring washer

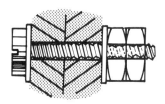

Fig. 47a Flat and spring washers

Fig. 47b A 'locking' nut

Permanent

Rivets are generally used to fix sheet metal parts together. They are a permanent fixing but can be 'undone' by drilling out the rivet. The two main types of rivet you will use in school are:

- the **snaphead** rivet, see Fig. 48.
- the **countersunk** rivet, see Fig. 49.

You usually use rivets made of the same metal as that being joined.

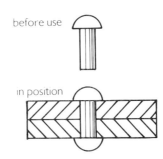

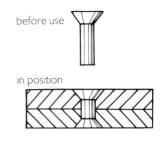

Fig. 48 Snaphead rivet   Fig. 49 Countersunk rivet

Snaphead riveting

A Bring plates together using the set tool which holds the rivet in place.

B Spread the body of the rivet with a hammer.

C Round the rivet with a ball-pein hammer.

D Dome over and finish the process using the snap tool which shapes the end of the rivet.

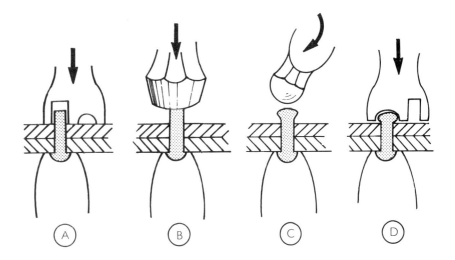

Fig. 50 Snaphead riveting

Countersunk riveting

A Drill and countersink holes.

B Place rivet in hole. Measure and cut off excess.

C Use a ball-pein hammer to spread rivet into hole.

D File off excess.

E Finished joint.

Countersunk riveting leaves a neat smooth finish.

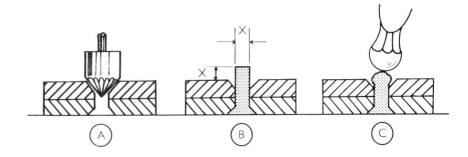

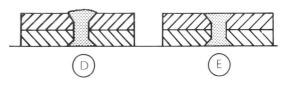

Fig. 51 Countersunk riveting

You Will Need

SOLDER

bar form

cored is usually pre-fluxed

FLUX

SOLDERING IRON

For soft soldering you will need:

Solder — a mixture of tin and lead.

Flux — apply with a brush and keep off skin.

Soldering iron — this can be heated by gas or electricity.

Fig. 52 Equipment for soft soldering

Soldering

Soldering is a method of joining metal together. When soldering a joint together you will need:

1 a heat source,
2 a filler material, i.e. solder,
3 a flux.

The types of soldering you may use are:

● soft soldering,
● hard soldering (brazing),
● hard soldering (silver soldering).

With all three methods the metal to be joined is heated to a temperature that allows the solder to melt. A **flux** is applied to the joint to prevent oxides forming. It also allows the solder to flow.

Soft soldering

Soft soldering is usually used to join tin plate and small size copper and brass parts. The solder used is a mixture of lead and tin and melts at around 230°C. It is known as **soft solder**. (It has a low melting point.)

Stages in making a soft soldered joint

1 Clean the joint with emery cloth and apply flux with a brush.
2 Dip the heated tip of the soldering iron into the flux, then into the solder. This is called 'tinning the iron'.
3 Place the heated iron on the joint. When hot enough the solder will flow around the joint. This is known as 'capillary action'.
4 Remove the iron and leave the joint until the solder looks a dull colour. Wash off any excess flux.

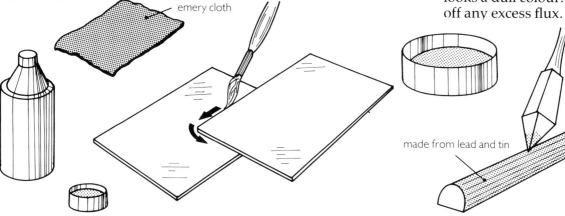

emery cloth

Fig. 53 Soft soldering, step 1

made from lead and tin

Fig. 54 Soft soldering, step 2

— Safety —

● Always work in a clear, clean area.
● Avoid touching your skin with the flux.
● Use the hot soldering iron carefully.

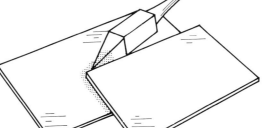

Fig. 55 Soft soldering, step 3

Fig. 56 Soft soldering, step 4

Hard soldering

Hard soldering makes a stronger joint than the previous method because the solder used is stronger and has a higher melting point (600–900°C). A soldering iron will not be hot enough to carry out this process. Therefore a **brazing torch** which uses a mixture of natural gas and air is required. **Brazing** is used only on *ferrous* metals. **Silver soldering** is mainly used for strong joints on copper or brasswork. Both types of hard soldering involve similar methods of working.

Stages in making a brazed joint

1 Clean the joint with a wire brush and emery cloth.
2 Place in hearth and build bricks up around the work. This helps keep in the heat.
3 Put flux on the joint. This is called **borax**. It is usually in a powder form and is made into a paste by adding water.

4 Heat the joint, gently at first so the flux does not blow away. When both pieces of metal are bright red, touch the solder to the joint until it melts and flows all around it.
5 When the metal has cooled to a dull colour, use metal tongs to cool the work in water. Clean up with a file and emery cloth.

You Will Need

Solder
Brazing — copper and zinc
Silver soldering — copper, zinc and silver
Flux — only use on the places to be joined.
Gas/air torch — heat source

Fig. 57 Equipment for hard soldering

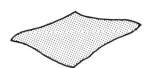

Fig. 58 Brazing, step 1

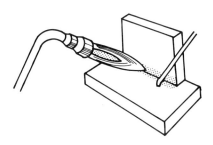

Fig. 61 Brazing, step 4

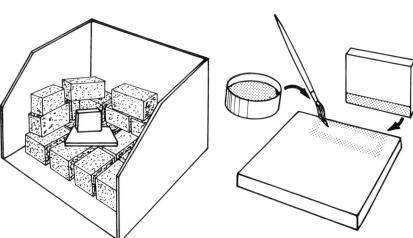

Fig. 59 Brazing, step 2   Fig. 60 Brazing, step 3

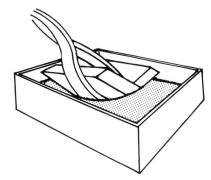

Fig. 62 Brazing, step 5

Checklist

For a successful result when soldering a joint you must:

● clean the places to be joined carefully
● use the correct flux
● use the correct filler rod for the work you are doing
● use a sufficient heat source

Safety

Do not use your fingers to pick up the hot metal.
WORK SAFELY

Assembling the material: wood

When joining solid wood together there are a number of traditional joints that you can use.

The advantage of a joint is that the wood is attached to itself and does not need any additional mechanical fixing.

Fig. 63 Different types of wood joint

1 Tee halving joint

One half the thickness of each piece is removed to produce a flat joint.

3 Dowel joint

Dowels can be used to join wood edge to edge or at right angles. It is usual to use more than one dowel to prevent the joint rotating.

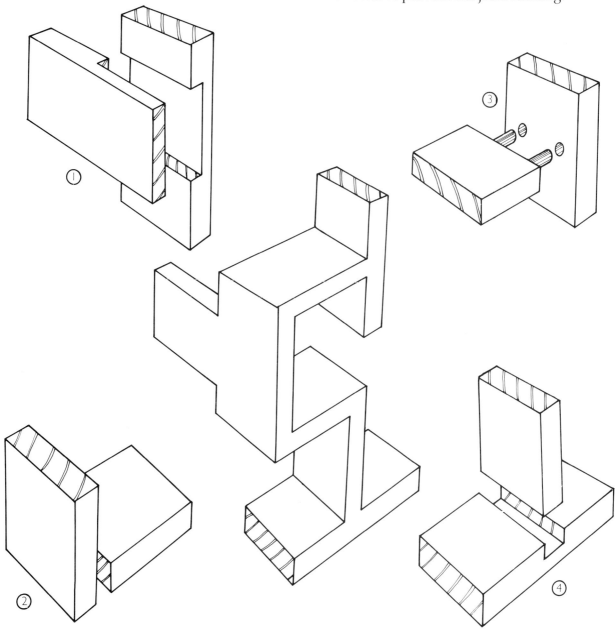

2 Butt joint

This joint relies upon the strength of the glue used to hold it together. Pins may be used to give additional strength.

4 Housing joint

This is a suitable method of jointing where you need to locate one piece of wood to another to stop sideways movement.

Wood can be joined using fixings made from different materials. These joints can be temporary or permanent.

Using screws and nails

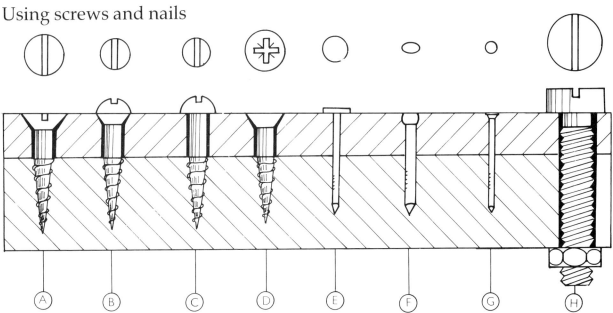

Fig. 64 Different types of wood fixings

A Countersunk screw
Use: General purpose. Head fits flush to the surface.

B Raised head screw
Use: Attaching fittings to wood. Often used with a screw cup.

C Roundhead screw
Use: Fixing brackets and sheet material in place.

D Pozidrive screw
Use: General purpose. Special head gives screwdriver a good grip.

E Round wire nail
Use: Construction work. Fixing sheet material to framework.

F Oval nail
Use: Any work where the head of the nail needs to be below the surface.

G Panel pin
Use: Fixing thin sheet material.

H Nut and cheesehead bolt
Use: For making joints that might need to be undone later.

> Always screw or nail through the thinner piece into the thicker.

Stages in preparing wood to be screwed together

1 Drill clearance hole.

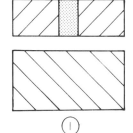

2 Drill countersink hole if required.

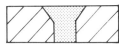
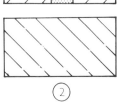

3 Drill pilot hole.

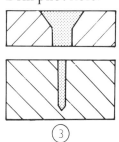

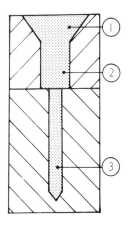

Fig. 65 Stages in screwing wood together

Screws These can be used to make permanent or temporary joints in wood. Screws are stronger than nails and can be removed without causing damage.

Nails Nailing is a quick and easy method of making a joint. As with screws, nailing should be used across the grain. If you nail into the end grain the joint will eventually work loose.

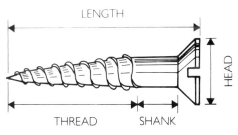

Fig. 66 Parts of a wood screw

117

Forming plastics

Vacuum forming

Vacuum forming produces such items as display trays and cartons. Large industrial machines produce plastic baths. A pre-heated sheet of **thermoplastic** is pulled onto a prepared former by sucking out the air from beneath it. A well-made former is important. Any faults in the former will show up in the plastic. Sloping sides to the former make it easier to remove from the plastic.

1 Air holes enable the plastic to be sucked over the former.
2 Put the former in the machine and clamp the plastic in place.
3 Heat the plastic until it softens to a 'rubber like' condition.
4 Remove the heat and raise the former into the softened plastic.
5 Turn on the vacuum. The plastic will collapse and take the shape of the former.
6 When cooled, unclamp the plastic and remove the former. Trim to required size.

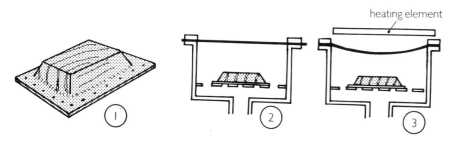
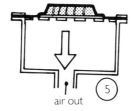

heating element

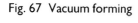
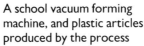
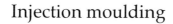
air out

Fig. 67 Vacuum forming

A school vacuum forming machine, and plastic articles produced by the process

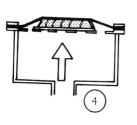

Injection moulding

This process produces such items as sink plugs, bowls and golf tees. *Molten plastic* is injected into a prepared mould.

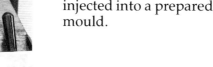

A school injection moulding machine, and plastic articles produced by this process

Line bending

You can shape thermoplastics such as acrylic using a **line bender**. The narrow opening in the line bender allows only a small part of the plastic to be heated at once. Its use is therefore limited to work which requires simple bends.

Forming a simple bend

1 Mark out the plastic.
2 Heat the plastic, turning over to ensure even heating.
3 When soft, place the plastic on a simple former and hold until it cools — see Fig. 69.

Ensure that the plastic is placed correctly on the machine. The part you wish to bend must be placed directly above the heating element — Fig. 70.

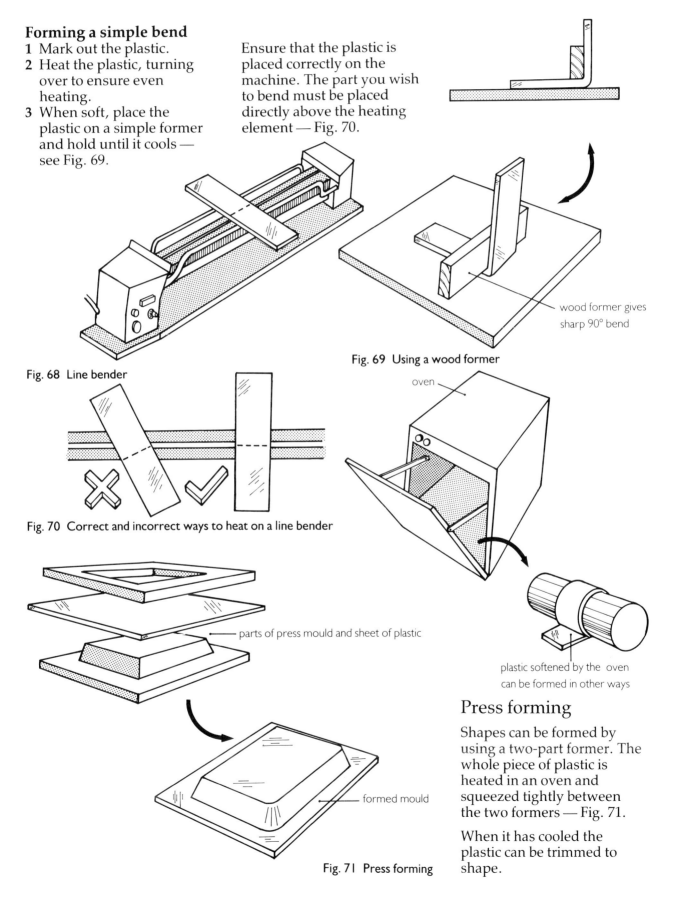

wood former gives sharp 90° bend

Fig. 69 Using a wood former

oven

Fig. 68 Line bender

Fig. 70 Correct and incorrect ways to heat on a line bender

plastic softened by the oven can be formed in other ways

parts of press mould and sheet of plastic

formed mould

Fig. 71 Press forming

Press forming

Shapes can be formed by using a two-part former. The whole piece of plastic is heated in an oven and squeezed tightly between the two formers — Fig. 71.

When it has cooled the plastic can be trimmed to shape.

Adhesives

The introduction of modern adhesives has meant that a number of materials do not need to rely upon a mechanical fixing, such as a wood screw, to hold them together. They can just be glued.

Below are some of the adhesives commonly used in schools.

Fig. 72 Table of adhesives

TYPE	TRADE NAME	USE	COMMENTS
Epoxy resin	Araldite	metals, many of the plastics	Supplied as two parts, an adhesive and a hardener. Mix equal amounts of both to form a consistent paste.
Acrylic	Tensol no. 12	acrylics, e.g. perspex	Apply to both surfaces sparingly and bring the pieces together quickly. Needs care in use — avoid breathing fumes and skin contact.
Polystyrene	Airfix cement	polystyrene	Supplied in small tubes to stick polystyrene to itself. Apply quickly and hold to set.
P.V.A.	Evostick 'W'	wood, card, paper, expanded polystyrene	White in colour and dries to a clear appearance. Work needs to be clamped.
Contact	Evostick	wood and laminated plastics	Glue is spread thinly on both surfaces. The surfaces are brought together when they appear to be dry. Useful for large areas.
Synthetic resin	Cascamite	wood	Water is added to a powder to form a runny liquid. Strong and waterproof when set. Work needs to be clamped.

Checklist

Which adhesive you choose will depend upon a number of considerations. These might include:

● Does it need to be waterproof?
● Does the work need to be clamped?
● Does the work need to be moved into position?
● Does it need to leave a clean finish?

 Safety

ALWAYS FOLLOW THE SAFETY RULES WITH ADHESIVES

Finishes

Before you apply a finish to a material its surface should be well prepared. For a final preparation various abrasive papers or cloths may be used.

Fig. 73 Paintbrush and spray can

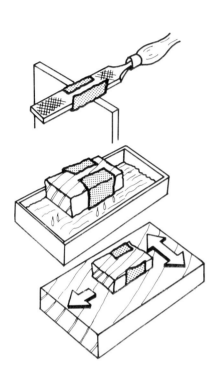

Fig. 74 Smoothing surfaces, steel, plastic, wood

MATERIAL	ABRASIVE	METHOD
Mild steel	emery cloth	Coarse, medium, fine grades. Rub in one direction. Wrap around a file for extra pressure.
Aluminium	wet or dry paper	Coarse, medium or fine grades. May be used with water to help smoothing.
Plastics	wet or dry paper	As above. Use on edges of plastics. Will 'dull' surfaces such as acrylic.

After preparing the surface of a material, a finish should be applied. This could be to enhance its appearance, or to protect the surface in use or from the elements, e.g. corrosion.

MATERIAL	FINISH	METHOD
Mild steel	Oil 'blueing'	Heat to dull red and immerse in an oil bath — Fig. 75.
	Plastic 'dip-coating'	Heat to bluish colour and dip into fluidising bed containing plastic powder — Fig. 76.
	Paint, e.g. gloss, cellulose	A primer coat must be applied first. Can be applied by brush or spray — Fig. 77.
Plastics	Paints, various types	A number of plastics have a high finish that does not require further colouring.
Wood	Button polish, polyurethane	Apply with brush. Dries quickly. May be clear, coloured; obtained in gloss, satin or matt finish.
	Stains	Apply with brush or rag. Water-based stains are more convenient to use.
	Paints, gloss, polyurethane	Apply with brush or spray. Water-based emulsion dries quickly.

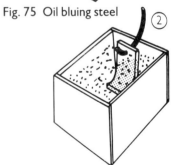

Fig. 75 Oil bluing steel

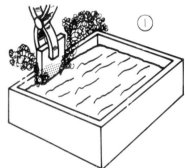

Fig. 76 Plastic dip-coating

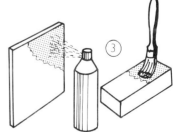

Fig. 77 Painting steel

 # Safety

It is extremely important that you pay particular attention to safety in the area where you design and make.

Everyone must learn and follow the simple safety rules. If one person disobeys the rules then the area in which you work can be dangerous for everyone else. Consider the general points below.

Eye Protection must be worn

1 Always enter the room sensibly.

2 Store coats and bags away from the work area.

3 Wear sensible footwear and protective clothing.

4 Store tools and equipment in a safe manner on the work surface.

5 Be considerate to others and always behave sensibly.

6 Do not interfere with the work of other people, or with machinery.

Fig. 1 Hazards in a workshop

Fig. 2 Pupils safety posters

More detailed safety rules are given later in this section.

Safety with hand tools

Here are some safety points for you to think about before you
carry out any practical work with hand tools.

Fig. 3 Removing a twist drill

Do not remove a twist drill by holding its cutting edge.

Fig. 4 Holding a chisel

Keep both hands behind the cutting edge.

Safety

ALWAYS THINK BEFORE YOU ACT

ACCIDENTS

**Report any accident to
your teacher immediately.**

Things You Will Try

- List all the hazards and dangerous practices that you can see in
  Fig. 1.
- List the safety points you should consider when you are
  designing and making.
- Choose one of the safety points from
  your list and design a colourful warning
  poster to display in your workroom.

 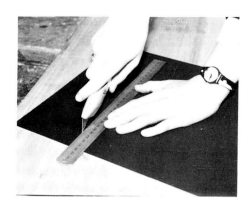

Fig. 5 Cutting with a knife

Keep your fingers away from the direction in which the knife will travel.

Fig. 6 Hammering

Take care not to hit your fingers when hammering.

Fig. 7 Sawing

Keep your fingers away from the teeth of the saw.

Fig. 8 Open window for ventilation

The working environment: remember that good ventilation is important if any dust or fumes are present.

Fig. 9 Soft soldering

When soft soldering, use a scrap piece of wood to hold the work in place. This will stop you burning your fingers.

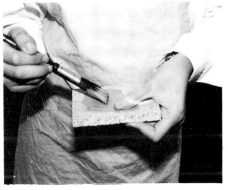 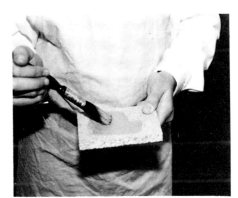

Fig. 10 Paintbrush

Try to avoid splashing paint on your hands. Some types of paint may be difficult to remove.

Safety with machines

When using machinery you must:

- Never use it without the permission of your teacher.
- Know what you are doing.
- Concentrate on what you are doing.
- Tie long hair back and tuck in loose clothing and ties.
- Never talk to someone using a machine.
- Always wear eye protection.

There are also specific points to remember with each piece of machinery.

Lathe

- wear eye protection
- tie up loose clothing
- hold work securely
- remove chuck key

Buffer

- wear eye protection
- tie up loose clothing

Brazing

- never point the flame at others
- use tongs to pick up hot metal, not your fingers

Drilling machine

- wear eye protection
- hold work securely
- remove chuck key

Disc sander

- wear eye protection
- cut off excess waste with a saw

Oven/line bender

- wear protective gloves
- do not overheat the plastic

Index